Urvashi Dave

BEAUTY RECIPES

Transcreation : Krupa Shukla

मूल्य : रु. 180.00

G 3263

PREFACE

It's a matter of great pleasure for us to put the **'Beauty Recipes'** in your hands.

Woman in India has equalled man in a number of spheres. She visits many places and meets many people. For this exposure, her personality counts a lot; and beauty is one of the factors adding to her personality. Therefore, for the fair sex, *'Beauty Care'* holds prime importance. Women all over the globe participate in beauty contests, viz., Miss Universe, Miss World, Miss India, Mrs India, etc., and Indian women have bagged quite a few awards. It has motivated the women all through the country to bring about awareness of *'Beauty Care'*.

We have tried our best to explain Threading, Skin Care, Hair Care, *Mehandi*, Hairstyles, etc., with due illustrations. Any beautician or a lay beauty-caring-person will be able to gain enough confidence to carry out *'Beauty Care'* herself.

We endorse the significant contribution of Mrs Urvashi Dave, the proprietor of Jasmine Beauty Care and of her daughter Richa Dave (who has to her credit the title of 'Youngest Beautician of India' in 'Limca Book of World Records').

Your constructive suggestions are warmly welcomed.

– Publishers

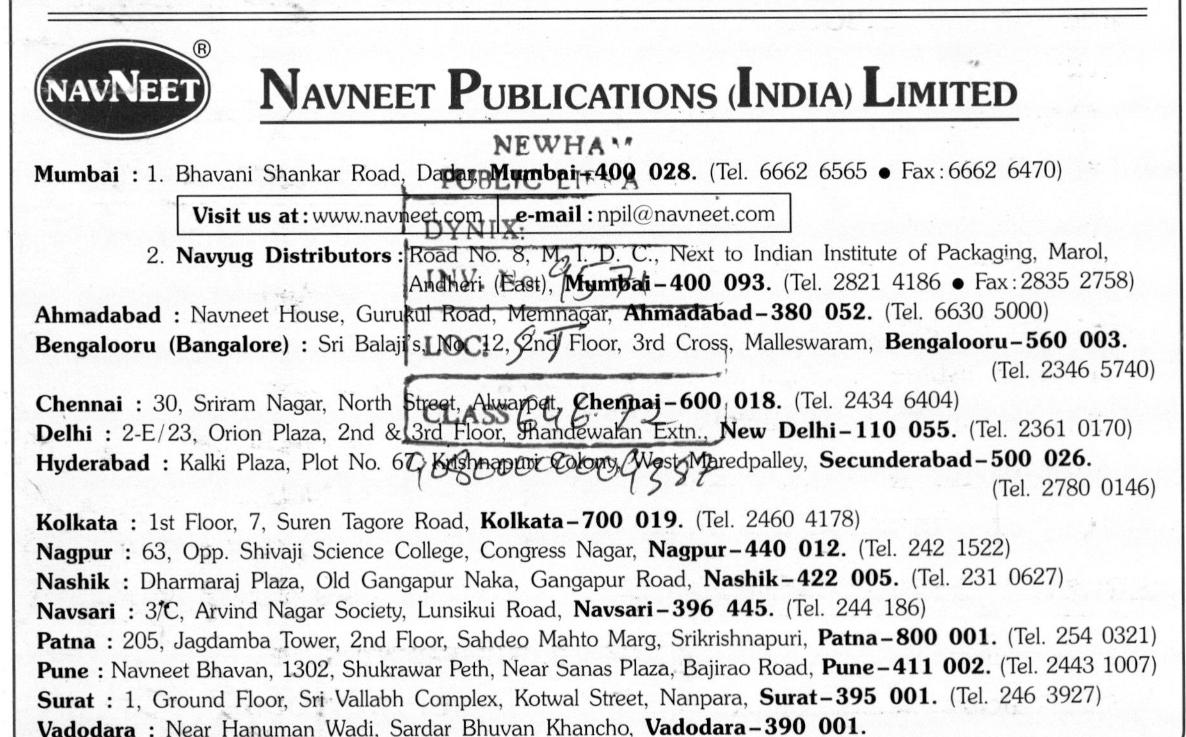

NAVNEET®

NAVNEET PUBLICATIONS (INDIA) LIMITED

Mumbai : 1. Bhavani Shankar Road, Dadar, **Mumbai – 400 028.** (Tel. 6662 6565 • Fax: 6662 6470)

Visit us at : www.navneet.com | **e-mail :** npil@navneet.com

2. **Navyug Distributors :** Road No. 8, M. I. D. C., Next to Indian Institute of Packaging, Marol, Andheri (East), **Mumbai – 400 093.** (Tel. 2821 4186 • Fax: 2835 2758)

Ahmadabad : Navneet House, Gurukul Road, Memnagar, **Ahmadabad – 380 052.** (Tel. 6630 5000)

Bengalooru (Bangalore) : Sri Balaji's, No. 12, 2nd Floor, 3rd Cross, Malleswaram, **Bengalooru – 560 003.** (Tel. 2346 5740)

Chennai : 30, Sriram Nagar, North Street, Alwarpet, **Chennai – 600 018.** (Tel. 2434 6404)

Delhi : 2-E/23, Orion Plaza, 2nd & 3rd Floor, Jhandewalan Extn., **New Delhi – 110 055.** (Tel. 2361 0170)

Hyderabad : Kalki Plaza, Plot No. 67, Krishnapuri Colony, West Maredpalley, **Secunderabad – 500 026.** (Tel. 2780 0146)

Kolkata : 1st Floor, 7, Suren Tagore Road, **Kolkata – 700 019.** (Tel. 2460 4178)

Nagpur : 63, Opp. Shivaji Science College, Congress Nagar, **Nagpur – 440 012.** (Tel. 242 1522)

Nashik : Dharmaraj Plaza, Old Gangapur Naka, Gangapur Road, **Nashik – 422 005.** (Tel. 231 0627)

Navsari : 3/C, Arvind Nagar Society, Lunsikui Road, **Navsari – 396 445.** (Tel. 244 186)

Patna : 205, Jagdamba Tower, 2nd Floor, Sahdeo Mahto Marg, Srikrishnapuri, **Patna – 800 001.** (Tel. 254 0321)

Pune : Navneet Bhavan, 1302, Shukrawar Peth, Near Sanas Plaza, Bajirao Road, **Pune – 411 002.** (Tel. 2443 1007)

Surat : 1, Ground Floor, Sri Vallabh Complex, Kotwal Street, Nanpara, **Surat – 395 001.** (Tel. 246 3927)

Vadodara : Near Hanuman Wadi, Sardar Bhuvan Khancho, **Vadodara – 390 001.**

INDEX

SECTION 1 : THREADING, WAXING AND BLEACHING

SECTION 2 : SKIN CARE

SECTION 3 : NAIL-TREATMENT

SECTION 4 : HAIR CARE

SECTION 5 : MEHANDI & TATTOOS

SECTION 6 : HAIRSTYLES

SECTION 7 : MAKE-UP

SECTION 8 : SAREE-STYLES

SECTION 1 : THREADING, WAXING AND BLEACHING

1. THREADING

Threading is a Chinese system of removing hair. Unwanted hair on some body parts sometimes come in the way of looking beautiful; particularly for women. In old days, women used flour, turmeric, etc., for removing hair. Today, there are many methods for solving the problem. One of them is **THREADING**.

* **Threading-kit :**
  - ➢ Thread No. 40
  - ➢ Talcum Powder
  - ➢ Cotton
  - ➢ Astringent
  - ➢ Scissors

* **Where Threading can be done :**
  (1) Eyebrows (2) Upperlips
  (3) Forehead (4) Side-blocks
  (5) Chin

* **Care to be taken before Threading :**
The unremoved hair after waxing can be removed only by threading.

- It is necessary to apply talcum powder before threading.
- Threading with a wet thread is less painful.

(1) Eyebrows Threading

Take the thread No. 40. Draw eyebrow-shapes on your leg where the hair-growth is more. Then press one end of the thread in your mouth and twist the other end around your fingers. Try threading (for the hair to be removed) from the opposite direction. Practise threading for one hour everyday at least for a week and you'll get accustomed to thread different shapes of eyebrows. The various shapes of eyebrows are as following :

Thin	Medium	Thick
(1) Arch-shaped 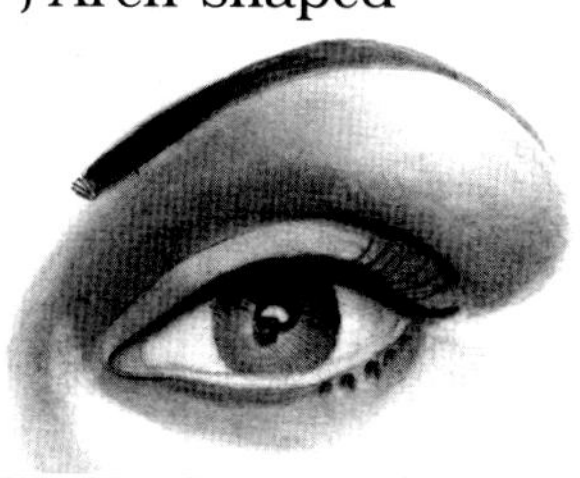	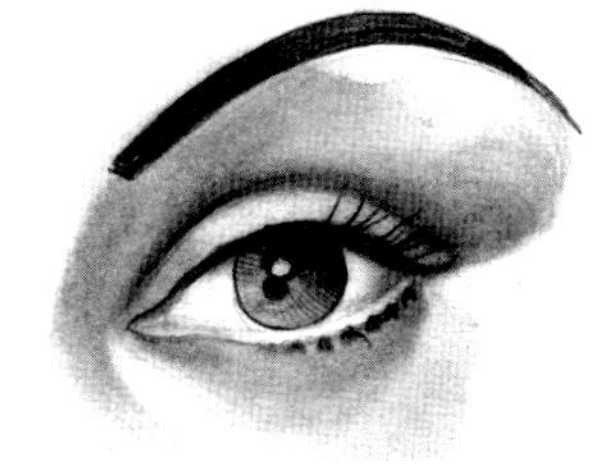	
(2) Curve 		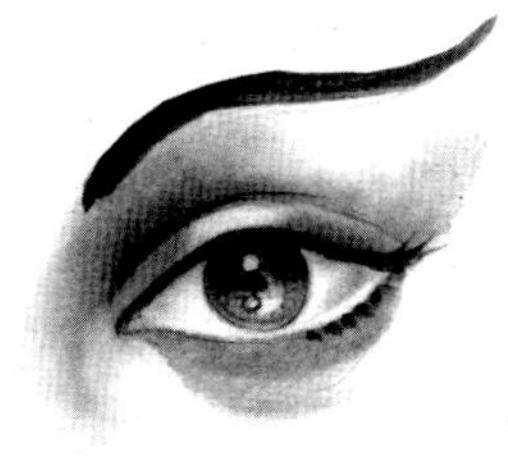

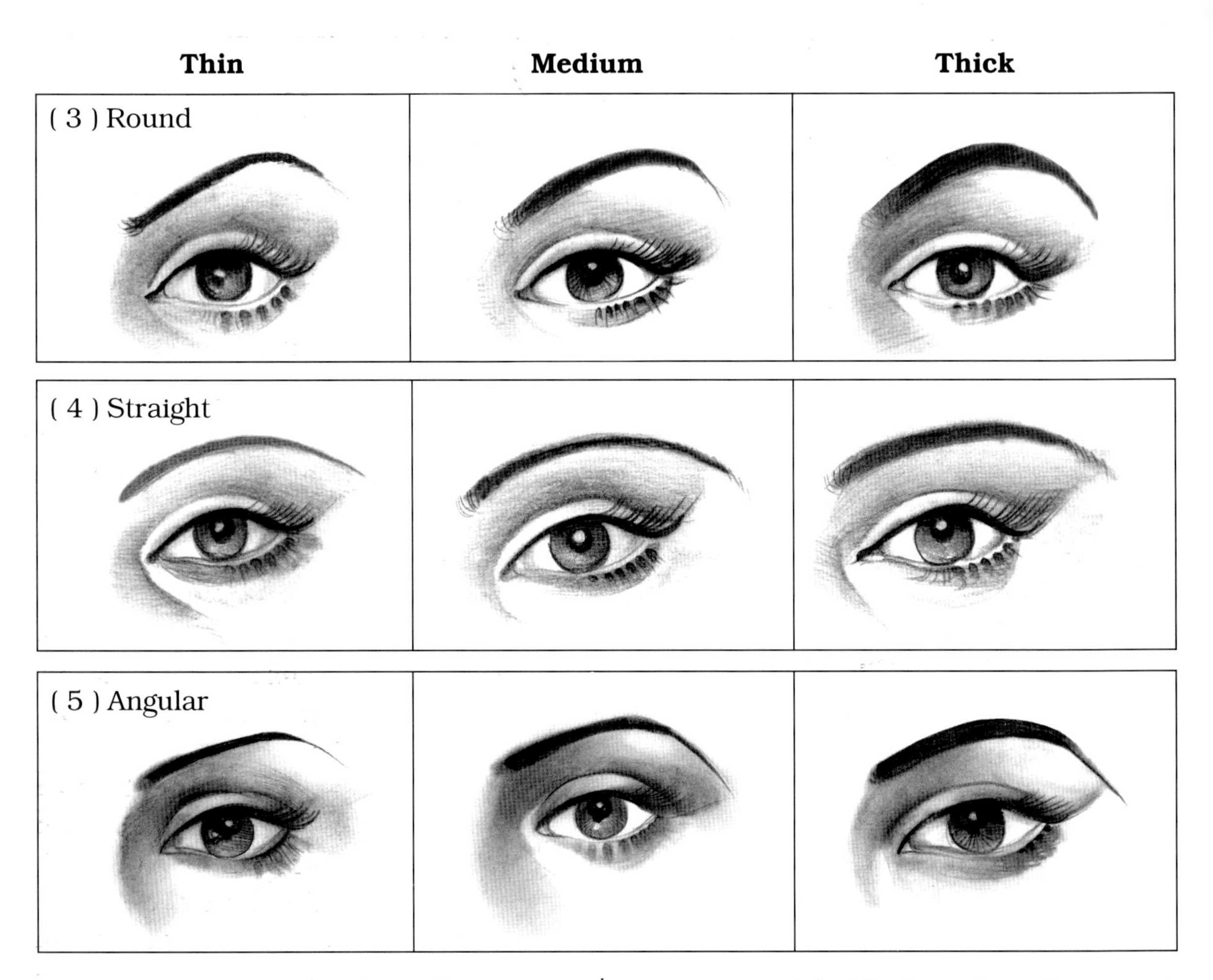

(2) Upperlips Threading

Lips are very delicate. If proper care is not taken while threading, the skin may get rashed. It is advisable to carry out threading after tightening the skin.

(3) Forehead Threading

Let the client stretch and hold the skin on the forehead tightly while the threading process is on. Carry out the threading in the opposite direction of the hair.

(4) Side-blocks Threading

Side-blocks means the area between the ear and the cheek. It is necessary to let the client stretch and hold the skin of this area tightly while the threading is in the process.

(5) Chin Threading

The chin is the area below the lower lip. Before threading, let the client keep the lower lip tight by pushing it with the tongue from inside.

* **Care to be taken after Threading :**
  - Apply astringent after threading.
  - If the skin gets rash after threading, massage it with a moisturizer cream.

2. WAXING

(1) Simple Waxing

* Waxing is another method of removing unwanted hair from the skin besides threading. Waxing can be done in three different ways. They are as follows :

1. Epilation :

This method of removing hair, includes threading, twitching and plucking.

2. Depilation :

Removing hair with the help of Hair Remover Cream is called Depilation.

3. Waxing :

Waxing is the easiest method of removing the unwanted hair. Waxing is more convenient to remove hair. Threading cannot help remove all the hair; while waxing helps do it. Waxing picks out hair from its roots and still it is not painful.

*** How to prepare Wax ?**

Take 250 ml of lemon-juice and 600 g of sugar in a thick metal pot. Put the pot on a low flame and keep stirring. Make the flame high after 5 to 6 minutes till the content boils over. Then once more make the flame low. Stir it for 2 to 3 minutes into a complete dissolve. A drop of the contents should make one single shred. Drop four to five drops of the contents in half a cup of water. If the drops sink below, take it for granted that the wax is ready. If they mix up with water, the content still needs more boiling.

*** Things used for Waxing :**

➢ Warm Wax ➢ Wax Heater
➢ Butterknife ➢ Sponge
➢ Water-bowl ➢ Powder
➢ Dettol
➢ Wax-straps made of cloth

*** Where Waxing can be done :**

➢ On the hands ➢ On the legs
➢ Under the arms ➢ On the back
➢ On the stomach ➢ On the face

*** How to do Waxing ?**

Apply talcum powder on the area where waxing is to be done. Then apply wax with a butterknife. Wax is to be applied in the same direction of the growth of the hair. Now press the waxstrip with equal pressure on the area where wax has been applied. Then pull it back in the opposite direction of the hair-growth. After the waxing, clean the area with sponge or cotton made wet in Dettol. If the skin is sensitive, massage the skin with calamine lotion or with cold cream.

*** Caretaking :** ● If both bleaching and waxing are to be done, go for bleaching first.

● See that the temperature of the wax is not so high as to cause any harm, burning, etc., to the person.

● If there are cuts, swells or acnes, avoid waxing on them.

● Refrain from using cheap hair remover lotion or cream available in the market. It darkens the skin and boosts up the growth of hair.

• For more cleanliness and hygienic precautions, use disposable waxstrips instead of cloth-straps.

(2) Flavoured Waxing

Sometimes people prefer flavoured waxing to remove the tiny growth of hair. For this waxing, only disposable waxstrips are to be used, so it is hygienic. Flavoured wax is composed of Hydrogenetic Vegetable Oil, Zinc Oxide, Paraffin Wax, Mineral Oil, Base Wax, Glycerine Rosynet and Titanium Dioxide. Various flavoured waxes are available suiting to different types of skins. For different purposes (as shown below) different flavoured waxes can be used :

➢ Orange wax – For skin-lightening

➢ Coconut wax – For anti-ageing effect

➢ Pink wax – For sensitive skin

➢ Lemon wax – For brown spots and wrinkles

➢ Almond wax – For dry skin

➢ Green Apple wax – For anti-allergic skin

➢ Banana wax – For lessening redness on the skin

➢ Chocolate wax – Anti-stress Spa-Therapy – For young skin

➢ Hazelnut wax – For smooth and bright skin

➢ Coffee wax – For tanning of the skin

∗ Method of doing Flavoured Waxing :

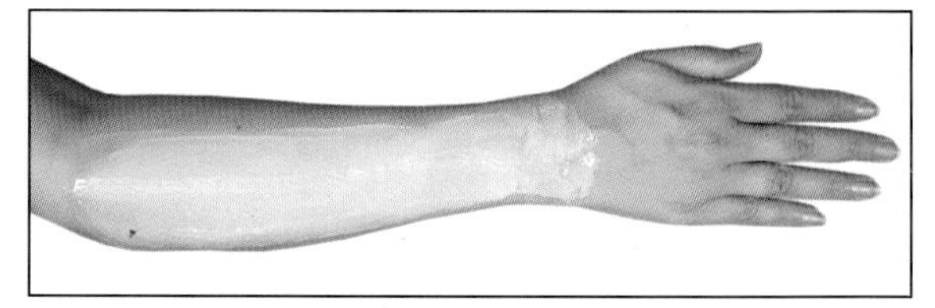

[Flavoured Waxing]

It is the usual practice of applying powder in simple waxing but here cleansing milk is applied instead. Apply wax in 2 to 2.5 inch-space on the skin and later strip it off with disposable waxstrip. Generally, after waxing, wax is cleaned out with water. But for this waxing, special oil is used for cleaning out the wax so that the skin does not get dry.

3. BLEACHING

Bleaching is a treatment for hiding unwanted hair. It lightens the darkness of hair. If the hair is less and not needed to be altogether removed, it can be hidden by bleaching.

* **Types of Bleaching :**
  (1) Cream Bleaching
  (2) Powder Bleaching

(1) Cream Bleaching

Cream Bleach is the most used bleach among all. Both local and imported products are available in the market. It is very easy to use the cream bleach. For general use, take more cream and less activator in preparing the bleach. For strong effect, more activator is advised.

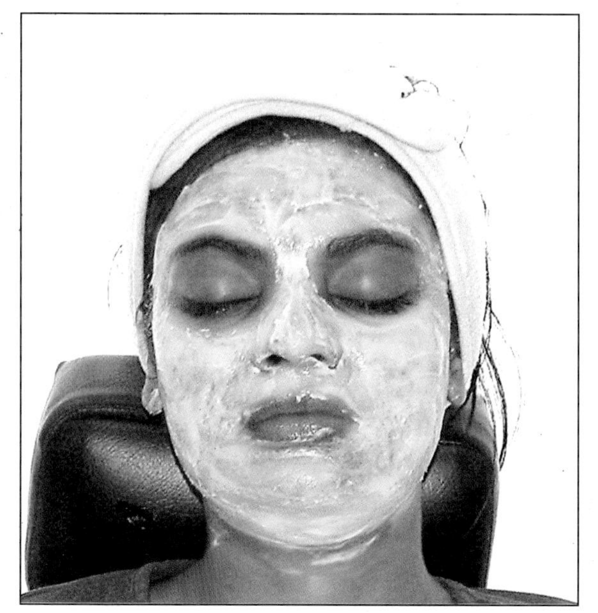

[Face with Bleach]

(2) Powder Bleaching

* **Ingredients for Powder Bleach :**
  ➢ Bleach Powder – 1 Tablespoon
  ➢ Ammonia – 4 to 8 drops
  ➢ Hydrogen Peroxide – As needed to prepare paste
  ➢ Antiseptic water – With Dettol or Savlon
  ➢ Cool water

* **Where Bleaching can be done :**
  ➢ On the face
  ➢ On the hands
  ➢ On the entire body
  ➢ On the hair on head

* **Disadvantages of Bleaching :**
  ➢ Ammonia is bad for the skin. It can cause allergy.
  ➢ The skin may turn dark in the long run.
  ➢ The skin may turn dry and rough.
  ➢ The possibility of skin-cancer also cannot be denied.

* **Caretaking :**
  • Don't do bleaching on very delicate skin parts.
  • Don't do bleaching on a cut or on a bleeding wound.
  • Don't bleach yourself. Get it done by an experienced beautician.

SECTION 2 : SKIN CARE

1. INFORMATION ABOUT THE SKIN

(1) Skin

A good beautician must know fairly well about the skin. New cells keep on forming in the skin and the old and worn ones go out of the skin from its upper layer. The cells keep on forming in the lowest layer of our skin. Skin is formed of hair, cells, sweat glands, oil glands, blood veins, etc..

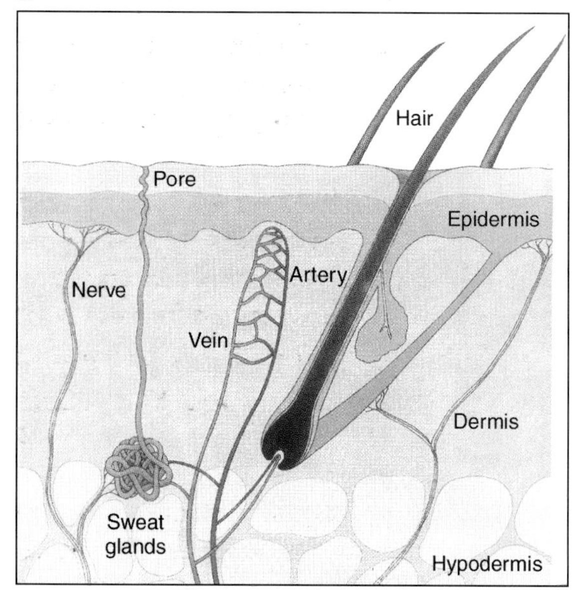

[Formation of the Skin]

* **There are three layers of the skin :**
  - ➢ Epidermis
  - ➢ Dermis
  - ➢ Hypodermis
* **Types of the skin :**
  - ➢ Normal skin
  - ➢ Oily skin
  - ➢ Dehydrated skin
  - ➢ Dry skin
  - ➢ Sensitive skin
  - ➢ Shallow skin
  - ➢ Combination skin
  - ➢ Mature or Aged skin

(2) Testing of the Skin

To know the type of skin the following three things can be taken help of :

1. Tissue Paper : Press a tissue paper lightly on your face before washing your face, soon after you get up in the morning. Then pull it off and examine it. If it has white flakes, the skin is dry. If there are drops of moisture or oiliness on it, the skin is oily; and if you find both of them on it, the skin is normal or it is a combination skin.

2. Soap : After washing the face with soap once more after five to ten minutes, if oiliness is felt on the skin, it is the oily skin. If the skin feels tight after washing the face with soap, it is the dry skin. The normal skin is dry in some parts and oily in others.

3. Litmus Paper : Press a litmus paper lightly on your face. If a blue litmus paper turns red, the skin is dry. If a red litmus paper turns blue, the skin is oily. If the litmus paper does not change its colour – blue or red, it is the normal skin.

(3) Functions of the Skin

➢ The skin protects from cold, heat, germs, adverse environmental effects, etc..

➢ The skin regulates the temperature of our body and balances it.

➢ The skin sweats out salts and other impurities of our body.

➢ There are a number of nerves just beneath the first layer of the skin. These nerves make us feel cold, heat, pain, etc..

➢ Generally, a skin comprises of acid and alkaline. If the amount of acid is more than alkaline, it helps avoid harmful effects of germs.

(4) Problems of the Skin

➢ **Blackheads :** Blackheads are the result of sebum deposited in the pores of the skin. Blackheads cannot altogether be avoided as they depend on the type of skin.

➢ **Whiteheads :** After the secretion of sebum, pores of the skin get blocked. They cause Whiteheads. Whiteheads are also called *Melia*.

➢ **Acne / Pimples :** This problem prevails commonly in young age because of the oily skin. Over active oil gland causes Blackheads and when Blackheads get infected, they turn into acne or pimples.

➢ **Allergy :** There is no common specific reason for the skin-allergy. But food, contagion, medicines, dust, smoke, chemicals, infection, etc., can cause allergy.

➢ **Freckles :** Small light-brown spots on the skin developed by the exposure to sunlight are called freckles. Freckles are found more on the fair skin. Keeping out in sun for long period aggravate the freckles.

➢ **Pigmentation :** Changes of melanin in skin and other internal changes in skin are the basic reasons of pigmentation. Light or dark round spots on the skin are seen in pigmentation. There are many other reasons, too, that cause pigmentation.

➢ **Dark circles under eyes :** There are many reasons for those dark circles under the eyes. Among them the outstanding ones are insufficient sleep, over strain to eyes, deficiency of vitamins, mental stress, diseases or illness, hereditary genes, etc..

➢ **Moles :** Moles are small and dark. Small moles sometimes add to beauty, but big moles are never appreciable.

➢ **Leuko-derma :** Leuko-derma is seen as white spots on the skin. These spots get larger with the passage of time. Leuko-derma is caused by the deficiency or lack of melanin in the skin.

For the problem like Leuko-derma permanent make-up, skin-grafting, etc., treatment can be sought from a good cosmetician.

➢ **Herpes :** Herpes is a disease caused by a virus that can make sore red spots appear on someone's sex organs or near their mouth. These spots are mostly seen in the corners of lips or on the nose.

➢ **Wart :** Wart is a small hard lump that grows on the skin, and it is caused by a virus. Wart is caused by over temperature of cell in epidermis or by spasman virus. It can be healed by taking proper treatment from a doctor.

➢ **Hypertrichosis :** The thick hair on the skin is known as hypertrichosis. It is caused by imbalance in hormones and secretions from glands.

For the cure of the disease like hypertrichosis, permanent hair removing is done with the laser system.

The treatment for the problem like leuko-derma, permanent make-up, skin-grafting, etc., can be done by a cosmetician.

2. FACIAL TREATMENT

Facial treatment is a very important treatment for beauty care. It relaxes the body and mind. The skin looks fresh and smooth after the facial treatment. It accelerates blood circulation. It tones up sinews. It activates passive glands. Facial is greatly advantageous for the dry and wrinkled skin. It balances moisture level of the skin. The facial treatment helps remove lymphatic worn-outs. It helps keep the skin young.

* **Things needed for Facial :**

➢ Cleansing milk ➢ Astringent
➢ Cotton ➢ Bowl
➢ Facial belt ➢ Facial apron
➢ Massage cream ➢ Face pack
➢ Apricot scrub ➢ Cold water
➢ Ice ➢ Napkin

* **Apparatuses used for Facial :**

➢ Steaming Machine
➢ Galvanic Machine
➢ Fairdick Machine
➢ High Frequency (Neon, Argon) Machine
➢ Vibrator
➢ Suction Machine
➢ Cold Steamer
➢ Micro-derma Braisen Machine
➢ Blackheads Remover
➢ Diamond-derma Braisen Machine
➢ Skin-lifting Machine
➢ Ultrasonic Machine
➢ Skin Tester
➢ Steriliser
➢ Magnifying Glass

* **Facial, Step by Step :**

➢ Cleansing with cleansing milk (2 to 3 minutes)
➢ Deep Cleansing with a scrub (3 to 5 minutes)
➢ Massage with a nourishing cream (20 to 25 minutes)
➢ Remove Blackheads after wiping out the cream (3 to 5 minutes)
➢ Apply astringent (1 to 2 minutes)
➢ Apply the face pack (10 to 15 minutes)
➢ Cold steam Oxidation (2 to 3 minutes)
➢ Protection with the skin-toner (1 to 2 minutes)

(1) Facial Steps

1. General Steps :

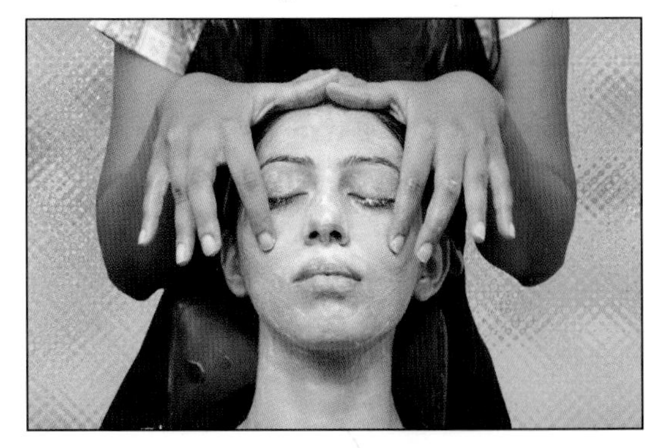

[General Steps]

➢ Apply cream with fingers on the face and the neck. Then take cold water in hand and follow the steps given below :

➢ **General Stroke :** Start from the chin with four fingers and go upwards passing by the nose to the forehead.

Then start backwards from forehead through beside ears to the chin.

➢ Massage upwards on the cheeks with fingers.

➢ Set two front fingers – one up and the other down – on the chin and massage as the scissors move.

➢ Massage clockwise and anti-clockwise around the lips.

➢ Then massage only clockwise around the lips.

➢ Massage half-circle at laughter-line.

➢ Massage clockwise and anti-clockwise below the noseball.

➢ Give a little pressure with two fingers a little below the eyebrow in centre beside the nose.

➢ Massage clockwise and anti-clockwise with two fingers at the eyebrow corners.

➢ Massage upwards on the nose tip with two front fingers of both the hands.

➢ Massage upwards on the nose-ridge with two front fingers of both the hands.

➢ Give a little pressure with just one finger on the tension-point.

➢ Give pressure with three fingers on the pulse-points (temples).

2. Massage Steps for the Cheeks :

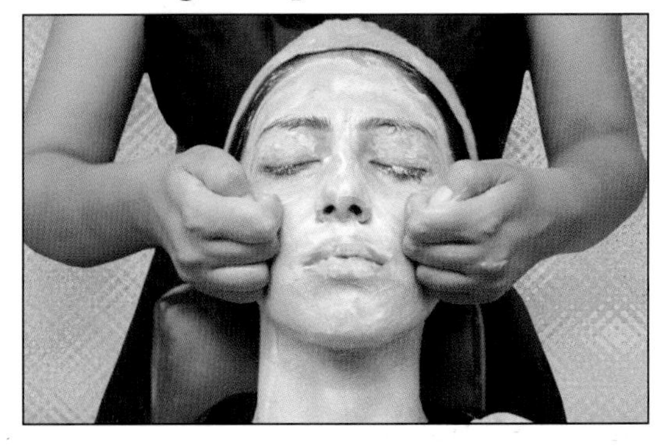

[Steps for the Cheeks]

➢ Do roll-patting with just one finger of both the hands from down to upwards.

➢ Do roll-patting with three fingers.

➢ Do pinching with both the hands.

➢ Do patting with fingers on both the cheeks.

➢ Set the hands like a Japanese fan and do vibration massage.

➢ Massage clockwise and anti-clockwise with the thumbs.

➢ Do vibration massage with all the fingers.

➢ Give pressure with three fingers on the pulse-points.

3. Massage Steps for the Eyes :

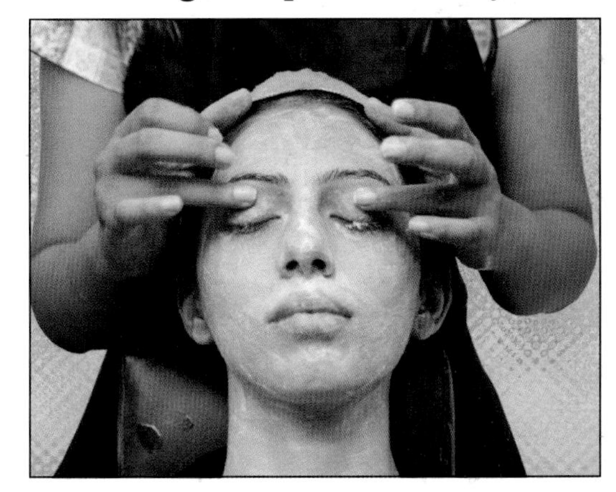

[Steps for the Eyes]

➢ Massage in clockwise and anti-clockwise mode around the eyes.

➢ Do vibration massage with fingers below the eyes.

➢ Massage clockwise and anti-clockwise on the eyeball with the third finger.

➢ Massage with only one finger on the crease-line.

➢ Massage in 'S' and '8' shape in the corners of the eyes.

➢ Do pinching massage on the eyebrows.

➢ Press the eyebrows.

➢ Massage in 'S' and '8' shape around the eyes.

➢ Keep the palms on the eyes for a while.

4. Massage Steps for the Forehead :

[Steps for the Forehead]

➢ Massage upwards with two front fingers in the centre of the forehead.

➢ Massage upwards with fingers on the eyebrows.

➢ Set two fingers horizontally in 'V' shape on the forehead and massage clockwise and anti-clockwise with one finger in the space between them (as shown in the picture).

➢ Once more make 'V' shape as above and do the friction massage.

➢ Keep the two fingers close to each other and massage giving a vertical stroke.

➢ Massage in 'S' and '8' shape on the forehead.

➢ Do the tapping massage by tapping all the fingers on the forehead.

➢ Do cupping with one hand and massage upwards with the other.

5. Massage Steps for the Jaw :

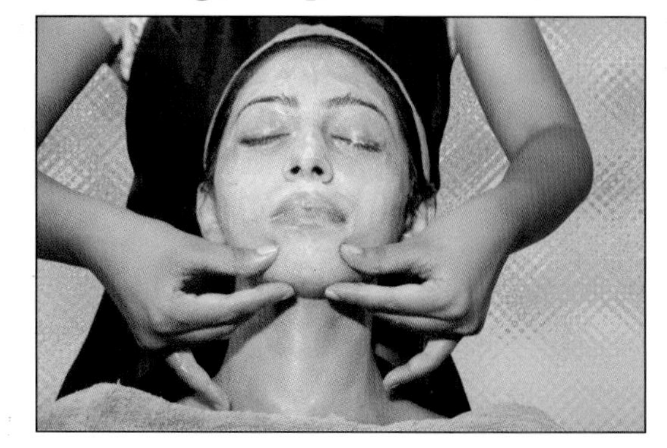

[Steps for the Jaw]

➢ Set one hand beside the ear and massage with the palm of the other hand up to the jaw-line on the neck.

➢ Do the criss-cross massage from the chin to the ear on the jaw-line.

➢ Do the pinching massage on the jaw.

➢ Do tapping with the fingers on the jaw-line.

➢ Do cupping with one hand and massage upwards with the other on the jaw-line.

➢ Do the light pressure massage upwards from the jaw-line.

➢ Do the criss-cross massage on the neck.

6. Massage Steps for the Shoulders :

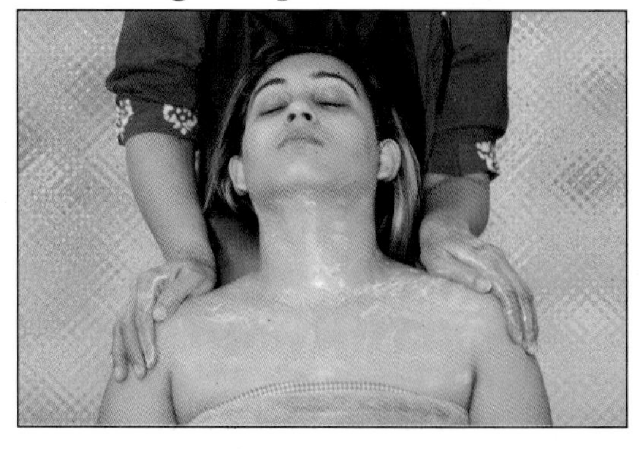

[Steps for the Shoulders]

➢ Set the palms wide open like the wings of the butterfly and do the circle massage.

➢ Do the vibration with both the hands.

➢ Do the friction massage in clockwise and anti-clockwise direction.

➢ Do the pinching massage on the shoulder.

➢ Tap with hands.

➢ Fold your palm and do the clockwise and anti-clockwise massage with the folded fingers.

➢ Massage inwards with the edges of the palms.

➢ Massage in 'S' and '8' shapes from one shoulder to the other.

➢ Press the collar-bone.

➢ Do the clockwise and anti-clockwise massage on the shoulder.

➢ Set one hand on one shoulder and massage upwards up to the top of the neck with the other hand.

7. Massage Steps for the Back :

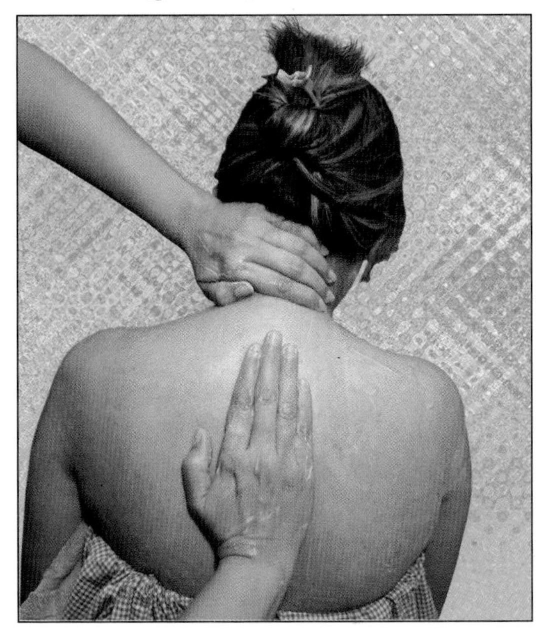

[Steps for the Back]

➢ Massage with the butterfly stroke.

➢ Keep one palm above the other and strike upwards on the spine (as shown in the picture).

➢ Massage clockwise and anti-clockwise on the occipital bone behind the ears.

➢ Set the palms wide open like a cat's paws and massage from down to upwards.

* **Caretaking :** Go on giving general strokes intermittently while doing all the steps as above. If you want to take cream or water, take it with just one hand, keeping the other on the face. During the massage, make it a point to give pressure only on the pressure points; while massage the rest of the parts with low-pressure. Take care that cream does not get into eyes or mouth. Massage on the hands and the legs till the pack gets dry.

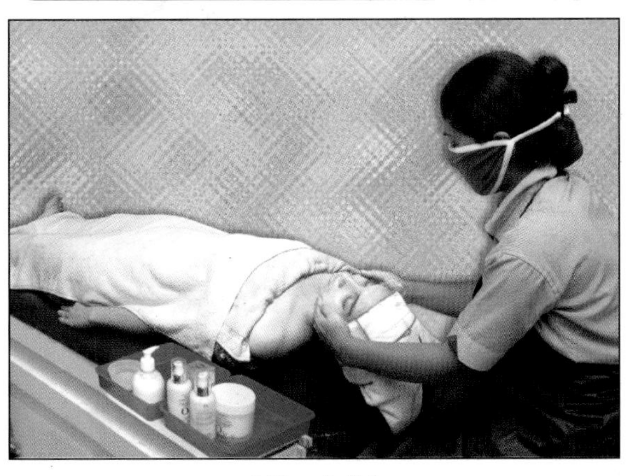

[Facial]

* **Caretaking :** Only common steps of facial-treatment and skin-treatment are given in this book. You are advised to follow the instructions or guidance specifically prescribed on each of the different products.

*** Basic Information about Facial Treatment according to the Skin Types :**

No.	Steps	Dry to Normal Skin	Normal to Oily Skin	Oily Skin
1.	Cleansing	Cleansing Milk in all seasons	Winter – Cleansing Milk Summer – Cleanser Monsoon – Derma Cleanser	Derma Cleanser or Mint Cleanser in all seasons
2.	Deep Cleansing	Scrub	Scrub	Derma Pill
3.	Skin Toning	Rosewater, Lavender	Rosewater, Lavender	Astringent
4.	Nourishing Massage	Herbal Cream Fruit Cream	Winter – Cream Summer & Monsoon – Cream + Gel	Derma Pill, Gel, Acne Cream
5.	Face-pack	Fruit Mask Peel Mask Honey Mask	Fruit Mask Mud Mask Milk Pack	Pimple Pack Tea-tree Mask Banana Pack
6.	Sun-protection Lotion	Sun-screen Lotion	Sun-screen Lotion	Sun-block Lotion

(2) Different Types of Facial

1. Simple Herbal Facial :

At first, as shown in the table above, decide the skin type, and then go for cleansing. Do deep cleansing with the scrub. Remove Blackheads and White-heads. Then apply the astringent. It is an antiseptic. Massage for about 20 to 25 minutes with the nourishing cream. If the skin is dry, apply a pack on the cream (without wiping out the cream). If the skin is normal, apply the pack after wiping out the cream. After applying the pack, put ice-cotton soaked in rosewater on the eyes. After the pack is dry, wipe it out and apply sun-protection lotion.

2. Shehnaz Herbal Facial :

At first, as shown in the table above, decide the skin type. Clean the face with Sha-cleanser. Use Sha-moon for the normal skin and Sha-rose for the oily skin. Do the deep cleansing with Sha-scrub. Then apply the astringent after removing the Blackheads and the Whiteheads. Massage for 20 to 25 minutes with Sha-life. Then go for the direct vibration massage on the leg and hand and the indirect vibration massage on the face. Give the cold compressor with Sha-rose. Give the cold compressor with cold steaming machine or with the cotton soaked in cold rosewater. Take 3 to 5 drops of Sha-fresh in Sha-face pack. Then remove the face-pack and apply Sha-base + Sha-silk in protection for the normal skin and for the oily skin. Apply more of Sha-base, and then less of Sha-silk.

3. Fruit Facial :

At first, do the deep cleansing according to the type of the skin. Remove the Blackheads and the Whiteheads and apply astringent. Then take fresh fruit juice of orange or sweet-lime and do the massage with it along with the galvanic (+) current for 7 minutes. Then go for the massage according to the skin type. Apply the fruit mask. At last, wipe out the pack and apply sun-protection lotion.

4. Vegetable Facial :

At first, clean the face and do the deep cleansing according to the skin type. Remove the Blackheads and the Whiteheads and apply the astringent. Then take the fresh vegetable juice of potato, cucumber, tomato, etc., and do the massage along with the galvanic (+) current for 7 minutes. The cream massage is done according to the type of the skin. For making the mask, grate potatoes, cucumber and carrot. Mix the face-pack in it according to the type of skin. Soak a gauge-piece in the rosewater, put it on the face and spread the prepared face pack on it for 15 to 20 minutes. Then retain the vegetable face pack on the face for 5 to 7 minutes. At last, clean the face and apply sun-protection lotion.

5. Gold-metallic Facial :

This facial is meant for the dry, normal or mature skin. Clean the face with the gold-cleanser. Then do the deep cleansing. Remove the Blackheads and the Whiteheads and apply the astringent. Apply the gold-metallic peel with the gold-dust. Apply the gold-dust on the problematic area. Retain the gold-peel for 7 to 10 minutes and then remove it with the friction massage. After that, massage the face with the hydro-skin polisher for 5 to 7 minutes. Don't use water while doing this massage. Without wiping out the gel, massage with the gold cream, for 20 to 25 minutes. If the skin is more dry, massage it with the skin-butter for 5 minutes. Then clean the face and apply the gold-metallic gel. Allow the massage with the galvanic or with the ultrasonic machine for 7 minutes on the gold gel. Then penetrate the gel into the skin with the hand massage for 5 minutes. Apply the gold-mask on it. Retain the gold-mask for 15 to 20 minutes. Clean the face and apply sun-protection lotion. It takes almost one and a half to two hours in this facial-treatment.

6. Silver Facial :

Silver facial is meant for the normal skin as well as for the oily skin. Clean the face with the silver cleanser after massaging for 5 to 7 minutes. Allow the deep cleansing with the scrub, remove the Blackheads and the Whiteheads and apply the astringent. Keep the silver-peel powder soaking in milk or curd for 7 to 10 minutes and apply it on the face. Retain the peel on the face for 10 minutes. Then remove it massaging it with the same milk or the curd in which the peel was soaked. Then apply the silver gel and massage with the galvanic (+) current or with the ultrasonic machine for 7 minutes. Keep on applying the silver lotion while massaging with the machine. Then massage with the silver gel for 10 to 15 minutes and apply the silver-pack. Remove the pack after 10 to 15 minutes. In the end, apply sun-protection lotion.

7. Pearl Facial :

This facial is advantageous to the normal skin and the delicate skin. This facial brings coolness. All the ingredients of this facial are anti-allergic. At first, massage with the pearl cleanser for 5 to 7 minutes and remove the Blackheads and the Whiteheads. Apply the astringent. Then massage with the pearl cream. Massage once following the steps as shown previously. Then while doing the massage the second time, massage on the face with the oil from the pearl-kit. Wipe out the face after the massage and apply the pearl-mask. Then wipe out the pearl-mask and apply sun-protection lotion.

8. Oxygen Facial :

Oxygen is very important for the skin. Oxygen keeps the skin fresh and alive. Oxygen facial makes the skin healthy and brings about instant glow in the skin. Oxygen facial charges the dull skin. At first, clean the face. Then apply the facial peeling cream and retain it for 10 minutes. Give the Ozone steam over it for 3 to 5 minutes. If the skin is more dull, let the skin have the steam for 5 minutes more. This peeling cream has very tiny granules of scrub. Give the steam and remove the Blackheads and the Whiteheads. Apply the astringent. Then mix the whitening cream in the oxygen cream and massage for 10 minutes. Wipe out the cream, apply ampule as required for the problem and apply the oxygen-mask. Cling the transparent paper (cling film) tightly on the mask. Cut it a little at the nose-cut so that breathing would not be a problem. Retain the oxygen-mask for 10 to 15 minutes. Then remove it and apply sun-protection lotion.

9. AHA Facial :

AHA means Alpha Hydroxy Acid. This facial brings lightening effect in the skin. The strength of peeling gel in it is almost 15%, so it brings about the tightening effect in the skin. AHA facial brings in immediate effect in the dark skin. At first, clean the face. Then massage it with the cream for 20 to 25 minutes. While massaging add soyabean or the mint gel in the cream. Soyabean gives Vitamins 'A' and 'E' to the dry skin. It is very important for the dry skin. Mint gel balances oil and water in the oily skin. Therefore, it is advisable to mix the gel in the cream. While doing the face-massage, wipe out the cream and apply ampule according to the skin problem and retain it for 5 minutes. Apply a thin layer of the glycolic peeling gel on it. If the peel causes a little burning, it is effective. Retain the peel for 10 minutes. To take off this peel, put a pinch of the baking soda in a little lukewarm water, and massage it out. Then massage on it with cold water in the beauty globe. Then apply AHA mask on it. If there are dark circles, apply the mask on the eyes too. Put a wet gauge-piece on it. Put cold cotton pads on the eyes. Retain the pack for 10 to 15 minutes. Then wash off the face and apply the intensive cream.

10. Shehnaz Thermoherb Facial :

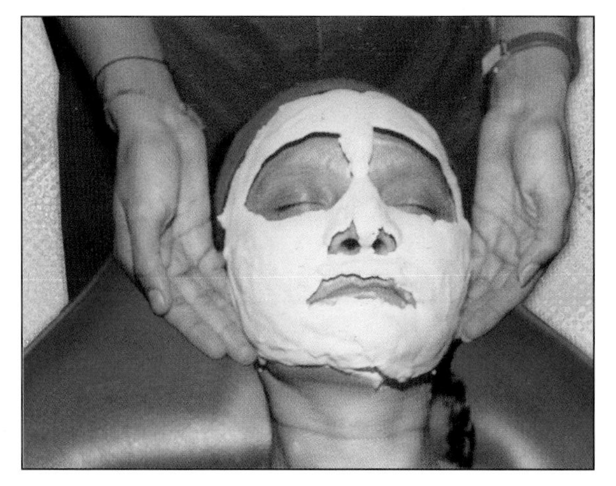

[Thermoherb Mask]

Thermoherb facial is advantageous for the dry, normal and mature skin. It is made of the base of Plaster of Paris. It brings about tightning effect in the skin. It balances oil and water in the skin. At first, clean the face with Sha-cleanser. Massage it with 15 to 20 minutes with Sha-life. Then massage it with the vibrator-roller and remove the Blackheads and the Whiteheads. Now, make a layer of Sha-life cream on the entire face. Mix the thermoherb powder in water and put a thick layer on it. Put eyepads on the eyes. Let the pack get dry for half an hour. While peeling off the pack, start from the edge and go ahead slowly. Then wipe off the face with the wet cotton. Apply the marrow-pack on it. Apply Sha-silk after peeling off the pack.

11. Green Apple Facial :

The green apple facial is meant for the thin, dry and delicate skin. This facial contains cleanser, massage cream, pack and toner. Clean the face with the apple cleanser. Do the deep cleansing and remove the Blackheads and the Whiteheads. Then apply the astringent. Massage the face with the apple cream for 20 to 25 minutes. This massage will help the cream penetrate into the skin and the skin will get moisture. Then wipe out the cream and apply the apple-mask. Wipe out the mask after 10 to 12 minutes. Then apply the apple toner.

12. Lemon Facial :

This facial is meant for the oily skin. At first, clean the face with the lemon cleanser. Then do the deep cleansing with scrub. Allow a little steam and remove the Blackheads and the Whiteheads. Then massage with the lemon cream. A little mint gel can also be taken with the lemon cream. Massage it for 10 to 15 minutes. Cleaning out the pack, and then apply the lemon pack after the massage. Apply the lemon toner and allow high frequency with the machine. Because of the high frequency machine the toner penetrates into the skin and the oiliness in the skin decreases.

13. Aroma Therapy Facial :

Aroma means fragrance. Fragrance has freshening effect on the body and the mind. The oil sought from the essence of vegetation leaves, flowers, roots, etc., is called Aroma oil. Aroma Therapy is also called Smell Therapy. In this facial treatment, massage is done with pressure points. The massage varies with the pressure of each finger. Two types of oils are used for this massage : (1) Carrier oil (2) Essential oil.

There is no fragrance in the Carrier oil. The Essential oil is fragrant.

In the Aroma facial, it is important to know which oil is to be used and in what quantity it is to be taken. Let's have a look at the quantity to be taken – both of the Carrier oil and the Essential oil.

*** The Quantity of Oil in accordance with the Skin Type :**

No.	Types of Skin	Cleansing	Deep Cleansing	Carrier Oil Drops	Essential Oil Drops
1.	Dry Skin	Aroma Cleansing Milk	Apply Scrub and Toner	Sweet Almond 30 mg Apricot 20 mg	Geranium 8 Camomile German 6 Sandalwood 6 Vertivert 6
2.	Oily Skin	Green Tea Face-wash	Apply Scrub and Toner	Grape-seed 40 mg Jojoba 10 mg	Sandalwood 7 Lavender 6 Myrtle 4 Rosewood 6 Paicholi 5
3.	Acne (Pimple) Skin	Rosewater+ Tea-tree Oil+ Lavender Oil Mix one drop of each, spray it and clean it with cotton.	No Deep Cleansing Apply Toner	Rosewater 50 mg	Lavender 3 Camomile German 4 Tea-tree 4

Prepare oil as suggested above and do the massage. Then apply the mask according to the skin type. Massage on the dry skin for 20 to 30 minutes. Massage on the oily skin for 10 to 15 minutes. For the skin with acne, do the pressure-point massage for 5 to 7 minutes. Aroma oil changes the mood with its fragrance. This oil gets penetrated into the blood soon and causes instant effect. It is advised to get an experienced beautician to do Aroma facial so as not to get its adverse effect. Use original and branded oils for this facial.

14. *Mehandi* Facial :

Mehandi is not only advantageous to hair, but it is equally advantageous to skin also. *Mehandi* brings about a cooling effect on the skin as it does in the hair. This facial can be done even at home.

* **Things used for the *Mehandi* Facial :**

➢ Cleansing Milk
➢ Nourishing Cream
➢ *Mehandi* Powder
➢ Rosewater
➢ Ripe Banana
➢ Betel Leaves
➢ Rose-petals
➢ Face Mask (According to skin type)

* **Method of *Mehandi* Facial :**

➢ At first, clean the face with the cleansing milk or face wash.

➢ Massage with the nourishing cream or any other cream for 15 to 20 minutes. Retain the cream on the face after the massage.

➢ Mix *Mehandi* in plain water or rosewater and prepare the paste. Apply this paste on the face with the cream. Retain it there for 5 to 7 minutes. Then clean the face with water.

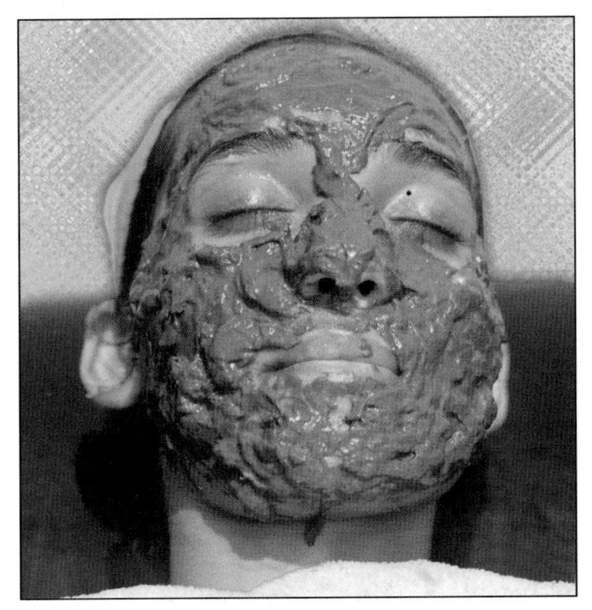

[*Mehandi* Mask]

➢ Massage with the fibred part of the betel leaf for 5 minutes. It will create heat on the skin and help remove the Blackheads and the Whiteheads.

➢ Crush the ripe banana. Crush the rose-petals in the palms, mix it in the crush of the ripe banana. Apply the paste on the face. Retain it for 5 minutes. Clean it with the wet sponge.

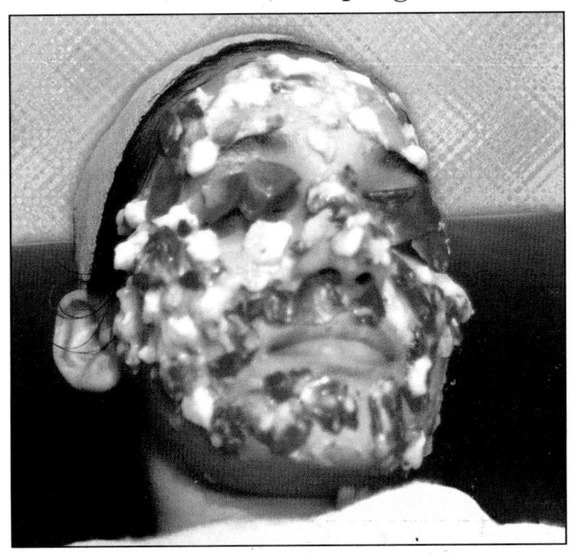

[Mask of crushed banana and rose-petals]

➢ At last, apply the fruit-mask on the entire face and put ice-cotton on the eyes.

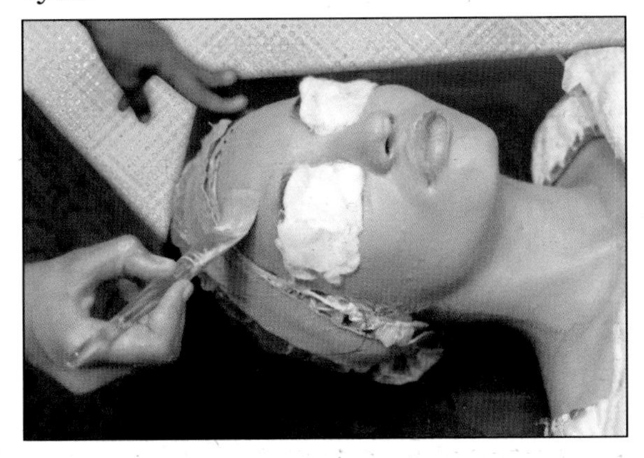

[Fruit Mask]

Banana is a very good tonic for skin. It makes the skin smooth, shining and tight. *Mehandi* brings about nice glow on the skin.

3. SKIN TREATMENT

Skin treatment means the treatment to cure skin problems. Some of the skin problems are : Sunburn (Skin gets dark in the sun), acnes or pimples, dark circles under eyes, pigmentation, wrinkles, Blackheads, Whiteheads, etc.. The following treatments are recommended for the above-mentioned skin problems :

(1) Galvanic Treatment

Galvanic Machine is a machine generating Direct Current (DC). It generates two currents : (i) Positive (+) and (ii) Negative (–). It helps penetrate gel or juice into the skin and skin problems can be cured. Two types of solutions are used for this treatment : (i) Alkaline Solution (ii) Acidic Solution.

No.	Alkaline Solution (–)	Acidic Solution (+)
1.	Mixture of half a cup of distilled water + one pinch of iodized salt + one spoon of baking powder.	The juices of orange, sweet-lime, cucumber, potato or tomato is Acidic Solution.
2.	Give negative (–) current with rod on the face and positive (+) current on the hand.	Give negative (–) current with rod on the face and positive (+) current on the hand.
3.	Penetrate Alkaline Solution in skin with the Galvanic Machine. It will melt the oil under skin.	Blood circulation will increase and the black dots and reddishness on the skin will disappear.
4.	Massage with the Galvanic Machine for 5 to 7 minutes on the normal skin and for 10 minutes on the acne-skin.	Massage with the Galvanic Machine for 8 to 10 minutes.
5.	Being melted, oil will ooze out and the oily skin will get dry to a certain extent.	The acne spots and pigmentation will decrease.
6.	Metallic taste may be felt on palate in mouth.	The taste of the juice used may be felt in the mouth.

1.Galvanic Ionization Treatment for Dry Skin :

➢ Clean the face by massaging with the cleansing milk for 5 to 7 minutes.

➢ Do the deep cleansing with the scrub and take out the Whiteheads and the Blackheads. Then apply the toner.

➢ Massage and penetrate the orange juice with positive (+) current for 8 to 10 minutes.

➢ Massage with the nourishing cream for 25 to 30 minutes.

➢ Mix 2 to 3 honey-drops in the face pack and apply it on the face. Don't forget to put eye-pads.

➢ After cleaning out the pack, give cold compressor with rosewater.

2. Galvanic Disincreation Treatment for the Oily Skin :

➢ Clean the face with the face-wash or astringent.

➢ For the skin with normal pimples, do the deep cleansing with the scrub and remove the Blackheads and the Whiteheads. Apply the toner. But if the pimples are full of puss and are aching, only apply the skin toner instead of doing the deep cleansing.

➢ Allow negative (–) current with the alkaline solution on the face for 5 to 7 minutes. Then allow the positive (+) current with the acidic solution on the face for 8 to 10 minutes. Don't allow the galvanic current at the bleeding spots.

➢ Clean the face. Apply the medicated powder and allow the neon high frequency current for 3 to 5 minutes.

➢ Clean the face with the astringent and apply the pimple pack.

➢ Allow the cold compressor with the rosewater or with the lemon toner.

∗ Caretaking :

● If a tooth (or teeth) has a metal cap, put a piece of cotton on it while allowing the galvanic current.

● When alkaline solution is to be applied, take care that it does not spread around the eyes and neck.

● Soak a gauge-piece in the alkaline or acidic solution, put it on the face and then allow the galvanic current. It helps the solution retain on the face.

● Don't allow the galvanic treatment to pregnant women.

(2) Skin Lightening Treatment

➢ Massage the face with the skin lightening face cleanser for 5 to 7 minutes and then clean the face.

➢ Mix the skin lightening pack in skin fair lotion and apply it on the face. Retain it for 15 minutes. Then wipe out the pack.

➢ Apply the oxy-pack. Put a wet gauge-piece on it. Allow the Argon high Frequency for 5 minutes so as to let oxy-pack penetrate into the skin.

➢ If the skin is more dry, mix the skin lightening cream in Vitamin 'E' cream. Then massage for 10 minutes.

➢ If the skin is still more dry, the other way is to apply Vitamin 'E' cream on the face and give massage with the ultrasonic machine. The ultrasonic machine helps the cream penetrate into the skin.

Ultrasonic is a micro current. This current is more advanced than the galvanic current. This current cannot be felt. There are two types of waves in this current : (i) Square waves and (ii) Alternate waves. Ultra waves bring heat to the skin and the skin gets soft. With the ultrasonic current massage on the eyes can also be done.

➢ Apply the skin lightening ampule on the skin, and then apply the skin lightening mask on it.

➢ After 15 minutes, clean out the mask. Then apply sun-screen lotion or sun-block lotion.

(3) Fruitpeel Treatment

This treatment is meant for the mature skin, pigmentation, wrinkles, etc..

➢ Clean the face with the cleansing milk.

➢ Mix honey with the apricot scrub and remove the Blackheads and the Whiteheads by doing the deep cleansing.

➢ Apply the skin toner.

➢ Retain the fruitpeel pack for 20 minutes.

➢ Give hot compressor with the cotton pad (cotton soaked in hot water) for 2 to 3 minutes and then wipe out the pack.

➢ Massage with the skinlife cream for 10 minutes.

➢ Retain the fruit-pack for 10 to 15 minutes. Keep ice-cotton on the eyes during that time.

➢ Apply the moisturizer after wiping out the pack.

(4) Non-surgical Skin Lifting

This treatment is more advantageous to the mature skin. Generally, for skin lifting, people who can afford, approach skin specialists. But this non-surgical approach is cheaper and advantageous.

How to go for it?

➢ Clean the face with the cleansing milk.

➢ Do deep cleansing with the scrub and remove the Blackheads and the Whiteheads.

➢ Apply the skin toner.

➢ Mix the mini-lift powder in activator and apply two layers of it. Apply the third and then the fourth layer after 5 minutes. Retain it for 15 to 20 minutes.

➢ Remove the mini-lift pack with the help of the skin-wash.

➢ Allow Ozone steam with the steaming machine.

➢ Massage on pressure-points with the skinlife cream for 15 to 20 minutes. Then apply the skin tightening mask.

➢ Apply the moisturizer.

(5) Acne Treatment

This treatment is specifically meant for the skin with more acnes or pimples. The High Frequency Machine is used for this treatment. High Frequency is alternative and mild current. It makes the blood circulation faster. This is an anti-bacterial current. The High Frequency current gives soothing, cooling and drying effect. The High Frequency current is of two types : (i) Neon (ii) Argon. The Neon High Frequency Current controls active sebaceous glands and sucks up the extra oily secretion. The Argon High Frequency Current helps penetrate skin toner into the skin.

How to go for it?

➢ Clean the face with the face-wash or with the alkaline-wash.

➢ If needed, remove the Blackheads and the Whiteheads by allowing steam. Then apply the astringent on the face.

➢ Massage the face with the mint gel for 5 to 7 minutes. Then wipe out the gel.

➢ Apply the medicated powder with cotton on the face and then allow the High Frequency Current for 5 to 7 minutes. If the acnes are aggravated or bleeding, don't allow High Frequency Current on it. If the pimples are big in size, allow the High Frequency Current with its electrode up.

➢ Clean the powder on the face with the astringent. Also clean the electrode with the astringent.

➢ Apply the anti-acne serum on the face and then apply a little thick pimple pack. Let it get dry. Don't remove the pack before it is dried completely.

➢ Apply skin toner after removing the pack.

(6) Skin Peeling Treatment

This treatment is done specially for pigmentation, scars (left after acne) and freckles. In this treatment, the skin is peeled with 33% glycolic acid. This skin treatment has rapid and long-lasting result. For the peeling, Diamond Dermic stud machine is also used. With this machine, better result can be obtained in comparison with other kinds of peeling. Normal glycolic peeling can be done manually (with hands). This treatment also helps removing scars (left after acnes) to a certain extent. The steps for glycolic peeling are as follow :

*** Method of Glycolic Peeling :**

➢ Clean the face with the apple cleanser.

➢ Allow hot compressor with cotton and remove the Blackheads and the Whiteheads. Then do the deep cleansing.

➢ Do the skin toning with the skin toner or with the spray-unit.

➢ Apply the glycolic peel on the face and let it get dry. (Take care that it is not applied near the eyes and on the lips.)

➢ Use the stud as need be and peel the skin with the Diamond Dermic machine.

➢ It is very important to neutralise the skin after face-peeling for this is a chemical peel.

➢ Apply ampule according to the skin problem and massage with an ultrasonic machine.

➢ Massage manually (with hands) if the skin demands so.

➢ Apply oxygen mask on the face.

The oxygen mask lets oxygen enter the skin. Peeling has removed the layer of the skin and the skin has got a little more sensitive, therefore the skin has become more receptive to the oxygen mask. Thus, with the direct absorption of oxygen, the skin looks healthy and lively. This peeling does not have any side-effects. This mask brings about lightening and tightening effect in the skin. This mask nourishes the skin. Therefore, at the end of the treatment, the application of the oxygen mask brings about 70% better result.

4. BODY MASSAGE

Body massage is very advantagous for the body and mind. It makes the skin soft, smooth and moisturised. Body massage boosts up the blood circulation and relaxes the body. Body massage reduces deposited fat-cells and stimulates the sinews. Body massage helps in nullifying aches in muscles and joints. It abolishes tension and tiredness.

In summer, body massage can be done with the body lotion or massage cream. In winter, other oils like – almond oil, sesame oil, etc., can be mixed in Aroma oils and massage with them. Generally, time for the massage is 60 to 80 minutes. After the body massage, hot-towel can be done. It opens up the skin pores and allows oil or lotion penetrate into the skin and balances water and oil. It relaxes the body from tiredness. The steps of body massage are as follows :

Steps for Body Massage

1. Steps for Scalp Massage :

➢ Heat the herbal oil luke-warm and apply it thoroughly on the scalp.

➢ Do the clockwise massage with all the fingers of both the hands.

➢ Do the rotation massage all over the scalp with a finger and a thumb.

➢ Do the pinching massage.

➢ Do the tapping and rubbing.

➢ Pull the hair from roots lightly.

➢ Do the criss-cross massage with the thumbs.

➢ Do the clockwise and anti-clockwise massage with the fingers on the occipital bones behind the ears.

➢ Allow butterfly strokes on the shoulders.

➢ Do the vibration and friction massage.

➢ Give pressure on the accupressure points.

➢ Massage in the hair with fingers as we comb hair.

2. Steps for Neck Massage :

➢ Massage with the fingers of both the hands upwards and give the butterfly strokes.

➢ Do the vibration and friction with both the hands.

➢ Do the pinching and tapping massage.

➢ Keep one hand on the neck and massage in 'S' and '8' shape with the other hand.

➢ Do the pinching and pressing to collar-bones.

➢ Do the clockwise and anti-clockwise massage on the shoulders.

3. Steps for Breast Massage :

➢ Do the clockwise and anti-clockwise massage.

➢ Massage upwards by turn with both the hands.

➢ Give a little pressure with both the hands and let it go repeatedly.

4. Steps for Hand Massage :

➢ Massage upwards by turn with both the hands.

➢ Do the clockwise and anti-clockwise massage on the contoured bones.

➢ Do the vibration and friction massage.

➢ Do the tapping and pinching massage.

➢ Form a circle like a bangle of both the palms and massage with them from upwards to downwards. It is called the Chinese Bangle Massage.

➢ Do the criss-cross and the clockwise and anti-clockwise massage on the joints.

➢ Do the massage from up to downwards under the arms.

➢ Do the pinching and tapping under the arms.

➢ Do the vibration and friction under the arms.

➢ Do the clockwise and anti-clockwise massage.

➢ Do the clockwise and anti-clockwise massage on the fingers.

➢ Rotate each of the fingers by turn and pull them one by one lightly.

➢ Hold each of the wrists in the other hand alternatively and do the clockwise and anti-clockwise massage.

➢ Massage the palm upwards with the thumbs.

5. Steps for Stomach Massage :

➢ Do the clockwise and anti-clockwise massage around the navel.

➢ Do the clockwise and anti-clockwise massage with both the hands on the entire area of the stomach.

➢ Do the vibration and friction massage.

➢ Do the pinching and tapping massage.

➢ Massage in the middle towards the waist with both the hands.

➢ Massage the stomach from down to upwards.

6. Steps for Back Massage :

➢ Massage on the back from up to downwards with both the hands.

➢ Do the vibration and friction massage.

➢ Do the pinching and tapping massage.

➢ Massage upwards from the waist to stomach.

➢ Do the criss-cross massage with the thumbs of both the hands.

➢ Do the criss-cross massage on the spine with the thumbs of both the hands by turn.

➢ Fold the palms of both the hands and do the press-massage.

➢ Massage from down to upwards with the palms on the neck.

7. Steps for Foot Massage :

➢ Massage with both the hands from down to upwards.

➢ Do the clockwise and anti-clockwise massage on all the joints.

➢ Pull slightly the hinder part of the sole / heel.

➢ Hold the feet alternatively and rotate it.

➢ Do the criss-cross massage on the joints.

➢ Do the clockwise and anti-clockwise massage on the hinder part of the sole / heel.

➢ Pull the toes lightly.

➢ Do rubbing on the toes.

➢ Do the vibration and friction massage.

➢ Do the pinching and tapping massage.

➢ Tap the hinder part of the sole with the folded palm.

➢ Do the criss-cross massage on the part below the knee.

➢ Do the upward massage on the muscles of the calf.

* **Caretaking :** Heat the oil luke-warm for body massage. Allow more pressure only on the pressure-points. Don't allow more pressure on the rest of the parts. If desired, the mud mask also can be applied after the body massage.

SECTION 3 : NAIL-TREATMENT

Nails are made of Carotene. Carotene is a proteinous substance. It exists in all the hard veins. Nutrition, health and diseases affect the growth of nails. Nails grow forward and upward. Nails grow faster in summer. Nails do not shed automatically and at certain intervals like hair. The treatment of the nails is equally important as that of the hair these days. Different types of manicure and pedicure are as follows :

(1) Manicure

Manicure is a Latin word. 'Mani' means 'hand' and 'cure' means 'treatment'. Manicure makes hands look nice. Massages in the 'Manicure Treatment' make the wrists smooth and flexible and prevent the skin of the hand getting wrinkled. It boosts up the blood circulation of hands and fingers. Manicure brings relief in arthritis, sinus, cold and cough. It also helps avoid worry and tension.

*** Apparatus and Material for Manicure :**

- ➢ Nail-cutter
- ➢ Nail-filer
- ➢ Cuticle Remover, Pusher
- ➢ Underneath Remover
- ➢ Dust Remover
- ➢ Sharp Dust Remover
- ➢ Cuticle knife
- ➢ Cotton
- ➢ Shampoo, Scrub
- ➢ Luke-warm Water
- ➢ Nail-polish Remover
- ➢ Massage Cream or Body Lotion
- ➢ Soft Hand-brush
- ➢ Lemon, Salt
- ➢ Napkin
- ➢ Finger-bowl
- ➢ Hydrogen Peroxide
- ➢ Manicure Mask
- ➢ Cling Film
- ➢ Cotton Gloves

*** Steps for Manicure Massage :**

➢ Massage upwards on both the hands allowing the general stroke.

➢ Do the clockwise and anti-clockwise massage on both the hands.

➢ Do the clockwise and anti-clockwise massage on fingers.

➢ Do the pinching massage.

➢ Massage with thumb from the middle of the palm towards fingers.

➢ Do rubbing.

➢ Pull the fingers one by one lightly.

➢ Massage in the palm with the folded palm.

➢ Do the clockwise and anti-clockwise massage on the wrists.

➢ Do the vibration massage.

➢ Do the tapping massage.

➢ Fold the palms in the shape of a bangle and do the massage.

➢ Do the clockwise and anti-clockwise massage on the elbow.

➢ Do the clockwise and anti-clockwise massage on all the nails.

*** Method of doing Manicure :**

➢ Before Manicure, remove the nail-polish and cut the nails if needed.

➢ File the nails and buffer them.

➢ Take Manicure shampoo, lemon juice, honey and hydrogen peroxide 4 to 5 drops each in the luke-warm water. Keep the hands in it for 10 to 15 minutes.

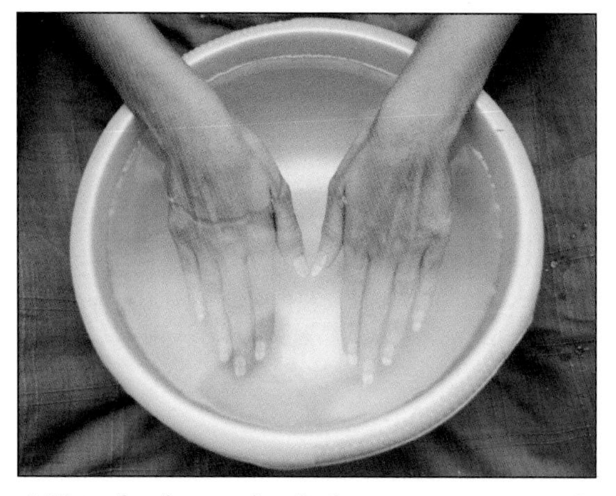

[Hands kept in luke-warm water]

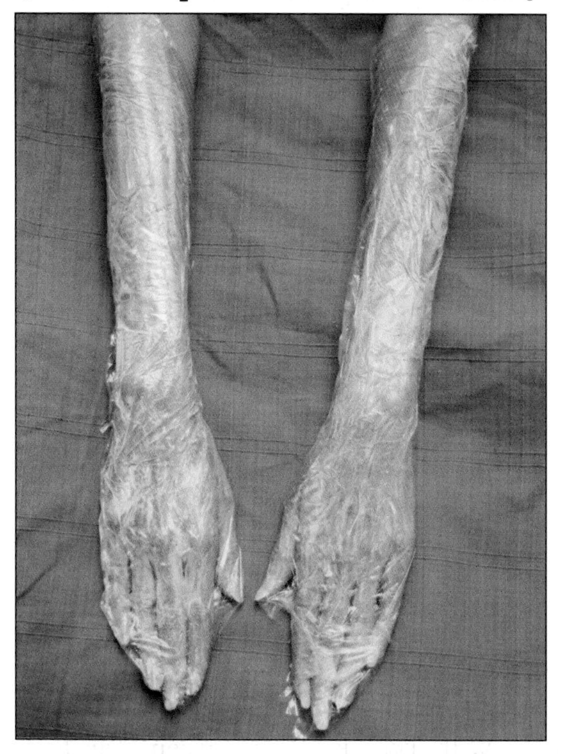

[Cling film paper on AHA mask]

➢ Do scrub massage lightly and wash the hands in the same water.

➢ Wipe the hands with a napkin and apply the cleansing cream on the nails. Massage only on the nails.

➢ Push back the cuticles with cuticle pusher. Then clean the cuticles from sides.

➢ Clean the nails with the underneath remover. Clean the nails from sides with a dust remover.

➢ Apply AHA skin lightening mask of manicure on the hands. Wrap the cling film paper tightly on it and put on the cotton gloves over it.

➢ Retain it for 10 minutes and then remove the gloves and the paper. Then massage it by rubbing. Make the person wash her hands in cold water. Massage will get the dead skin removed.

➢ Take massage steps with the cream or body lotion as mentioned on the page No. 36 Massage for 5 to 10 minutes. Wipe out the cream from inside of the nails and apply the basecoat nail-polish.

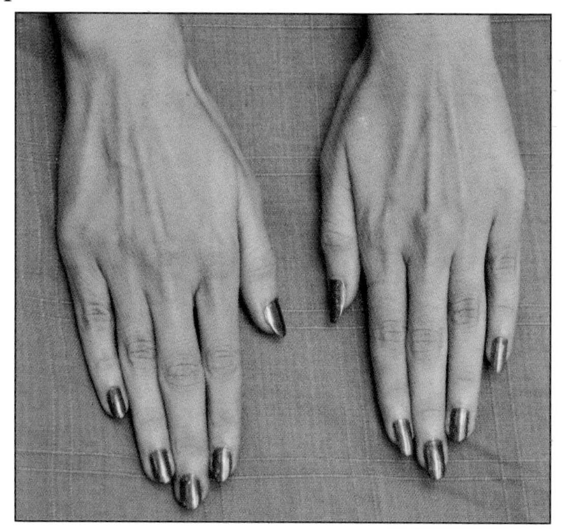

[Nail-polish after Manicure]

(2) Pedicure

The treatment of legs is Pedicure. This treatment comprises the treatment of the hinder part of the sole, nails and the leg. It keeps the legs in good condition by boosting up the blood circulation. The sinews of the legs get stimulated. It makes the skin smooth and provides the legs a beauty.

∗ Apparatus and Material used in Pedicure :

- ➢ Small scissors ➢ Nail-cutter
- ➢ Pumice Stone ➢ Scraper
- ➢ Pedi-cutter ➢ Orange Stick
- ➢ Nail-filer ➢ Cuticle Pusher
- ➢ Underneath Dust Remover
- ➢ Cuticle knife
- ➢ Soft nail-brush
- ➢ Luke-warm water
- ➢ Nail-polish Remover
- ➢ Foot-spa
- ➢ Napkin

∗ Steps for Pedicure Massage :

➢ Massage upwards on the leg with both the hands.

➢ Do the clockwise and anti-clockwise massage on the toes.

➢ Bend the toes and pull them tightly.

➢ Rotate each of the toes clockwise and anti-clockwise one by one and pull them.

➢ Do the criss-cross massage under the toes on the sole.

➢ Do clockwise and anti-clockwise massage with the folded palm on the sole.

➢ Massage on the heel.

➢ Massage in 'S' and '8' shape on the sole of the foot.

➢ Do the criss-cross massage around the ankle-joint of the foot.

➢ Do the vibration massage with both the hands on the foot.

➢ Do the pinching massage.

➢ Do tapping with the fingers of both the hands.

➢ Fold the palms round together in the shape of a bangle and do the massage.

➢ Do the criss-cross massage below the knee-joints.

➢ Do the circle massage around the knee.

➢ Massage upwards on the calf-muscles.

➢ Do general stroke massage at the last.

∗ Method of doing Pedicure :

➢ Remove the nail-polish before the pedicure. Trim the toe-nails straight across with a nail-clipper or scissors.

➢ Then file from the edges towards the centre of your nails. Buffer the nails.

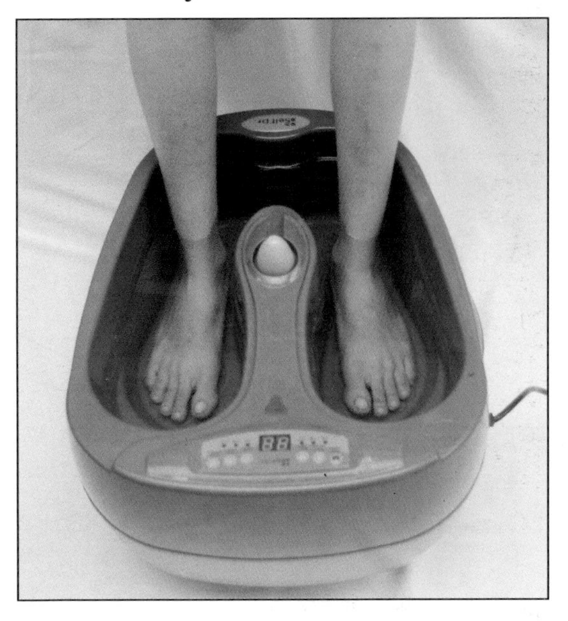

[Feet soaked in the Foot-spa]

➢ Soak the feet in warm water with shampoo, lemon drops and 5 to 7 drops of hydrogen peroxide. Retain them in the foot-spa for 10 minutes.

➢ Remove the dirt from the nails and from the hinder part of the sole with a soft brush.

➢ Remove the dead skin of the hinder part of the sole with a scraper. If there are cuts and the dead skin is more, remove the extra skin with the pedi-cutter.

➢ Rub pumice stone lightly on the leg.

➢ Massage with the scrub for 2 to 3 minutes and wash the legs in the same warm water. Then wipe out the legs and apply the cleansing cream on the nails.

➢ Push back the cuticles with the cuticle pusher and clean the cuticles. Remove extra cuticles.

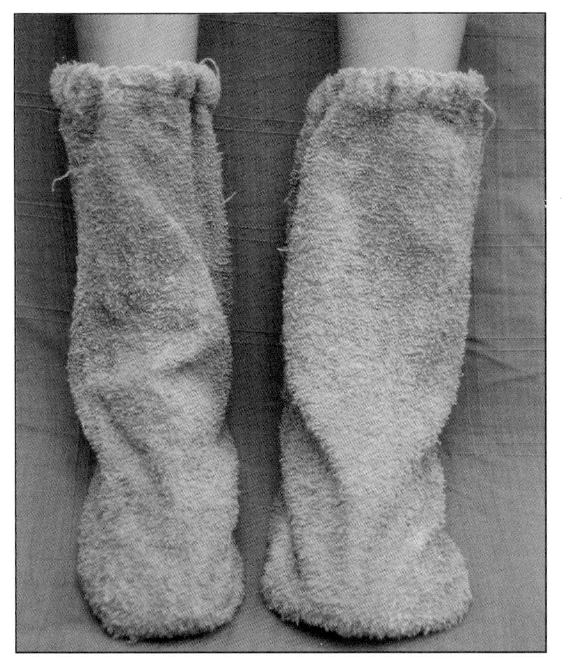

[Cotton socks over the cling film]

➢ Apply the pedicure mask. Wrap the cling film tightly on it and put on the cotton socks over it. Let the socks remain for about 10 minutes.

➢ Take off the socks, remove the cling film and the mask rub. Then wash the feet.

➢ Do massage with the body lotion or cream following the steps suggested on page No. 38 for 7 to 10 minutes.

➢ Wipe out the cream from the nails and apply the basecoat. Then the nail-polish of choice can be applied.

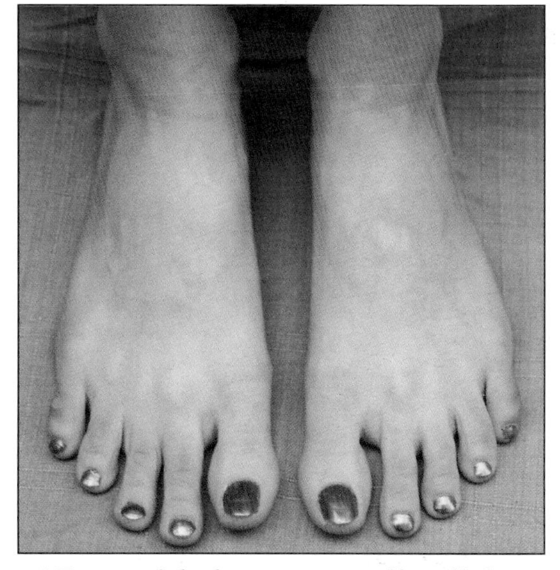

[Feet with basecoat nail-polish]

(3) French Manicure

French manicure differs a little from the common manicure. Nails are given square shape in this manicure. Then nails are cleaned as is done in common manicure. Paraffin wax mask is applied instead of the manicure mask. Paraffin wax mask is prepared in base. It is heated in the wax-heater. The special wax-heater for paraffin is also available, in which hands are soaked in the hot wax. If there is no special wax-heater, paraffin wax is heated in simple wax-heater and it is applied with a brush. Peel it off after 10 minutes and massage with cream or body lotion according to the steps suggested previously. Wipe out the nails and apply the basecoat nail-polish. French nail-polish is done as shown in the picture given on the next page :

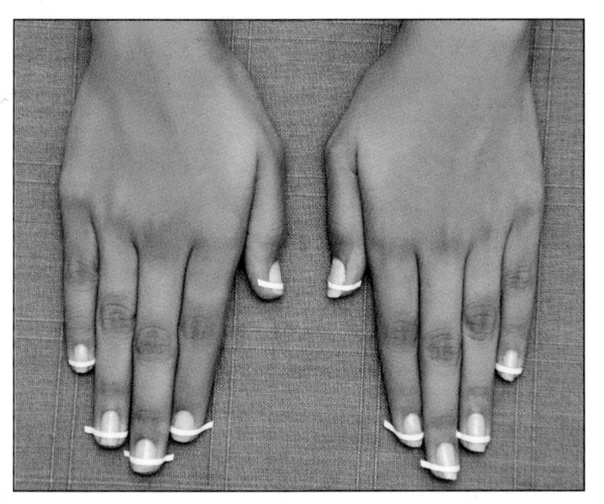

[French tips before nail-polish]

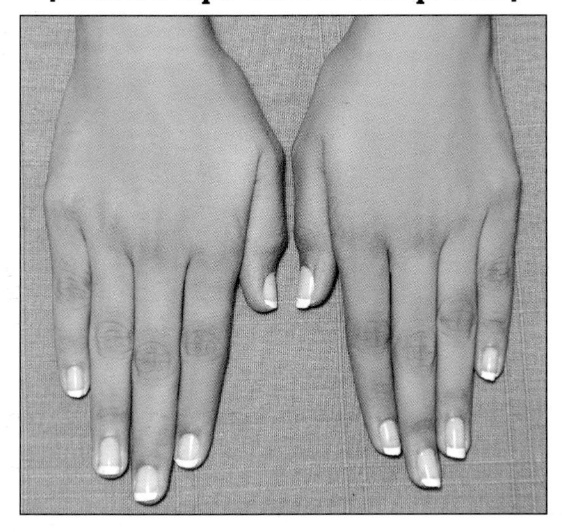

[Hands after French nail-polish]

Top-coat is done after it gets dry. The manicure nail-polish kit is easily available in the market. If the toes are long, the same method can also be taken help of for pedicure.

(4) Chocolate Manicure – Pedicure

This is a new method. In this method, also manicure and pedicure can be done as suggested previously. The chocolate base mask is applied in this method.

This mask is made up of chocolate + paraffin purified wax + herbs + oxygenating agent. It gives the skin nourishment and softness. It improves skin texture by removing the wrinkles of the skin. This mask does not give the lightening effect. This mask rejuvenates the dehydrated skin. The chocolate mask is different for the young skin and the mature skin. For the young skin, it is chocolate with mint and for the mature skin, it is the Swiss chocolate mask.

* **Method of applying Chocolate Mask :**

The Chocolate mask is comparatively very hard. Therefore, before applying, it is heated in wax-heater and then applied with a brush. After applying the mask, the cling film is wrapped on it. After 5 minutes, the hot compressor is given on the mask for 2 to 3 minutes. Hot compressor can be allowed twice as this mask is to be retained for 20 minutes. Wipe out the cream or the lotion of the massage and then give the massage. Hands are not to be washed after removing the massage.

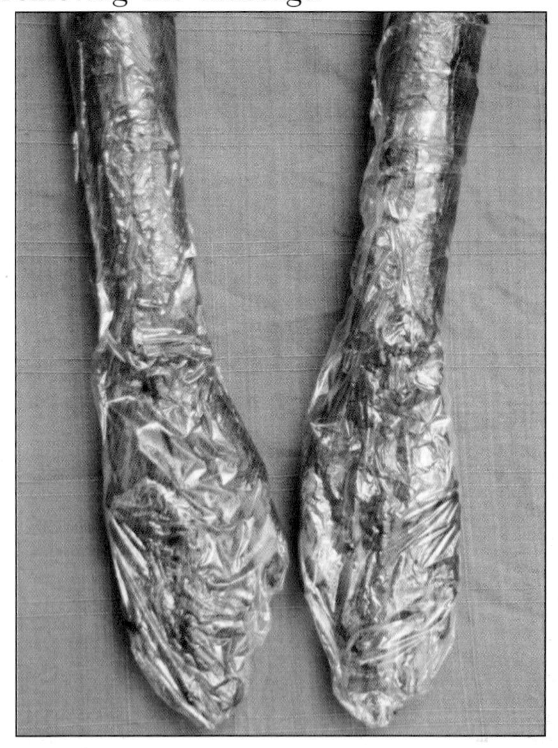

[Cling film paper on Chocolate Mask]

SECTION 4 : HAIR CARE

1. HAIR CARE

(1) Hair

Hair is made of protein known as Carotene. The hair is divided into three layers : (i) Cuticle, (ii) Cortex and (iii) Medulla. The exterior layer of hair is known as Cuticle. It gives protection and shining to the hair. Cortex is the middle layer. It is the most important layer where certain chemical changes take place. The substance, melanin, in it gives colour to the hair. Medulla is the innermost layer of the hair. It carries nutrients to the cuticle and the cortex.

(2) Types of Hair

(1) Normal Hair (2) Oily Hair (3) Dry Hair

* **Hair Problems :**

➢ White hair ➢ Falling of hair
➢ Dandruff ➢ Leuco-derma *(Undari)*

(3) Reasons of Hair Problems

➢ Worry, tension and convulsion

➢ Scalp infection

➢ Hormonal disturbance

➢ Malnutrition, Deficiency of vitamins and minerals

➢ Side-effects of medicines

➢ Improper treatment of hair

➢ Overuse of harsh shampoo

➢ Use of dirty or used towels, pillow-covers, combs and brush

(4) Hot Oil Massage

Massage is important for strong and healthy hair. Massage boosts up the blood circulation of the head and prevents falling of hair. It gives nutrition to the hair-roots and the hair looks clean and shiny. Dandruff can also be removed by oil massage. Regular hair massage makes hair shining, healthy and thick. Oil massage also brings mental peace.

* **Apparatus and Materials for Oil Massage :**

➢ Hair Oil ➢ Oil Heater
➢ Comb ➢ Cotton ➢ Towel

* **Steps for Oil Massage :**

➢ Massage with all the fingers.

➢ Do the clockwise and anti-clockwise massage with the thumbs and fingers.

➢ Allow pressure on the head and release it. This process is to be repeated for 8 to 10 time.

➢ Part the hair here and there and do the pinching massage.

➢ Put both the palms together and do the tapping massage.

➢ Part the hair in strands. Twist them around the fingers and pull them lightly.

➢ Do the criss-cross massage with the thumbs.

➢ Hold hands in the vertical position and do the tapping with fingers.

➢ Do the clockwise and anti-clockwise massage on the occipital bone behind ears.

➢ Run fingers through the hair and rub on the scalp with the palms.

➢ Do the clockwise and anti-clockwise massage on the shoulders.

➢ Keep the fingers wide open like the butterfly-wings and massage on the back.

➢ Do the vibration massage on the back.

➢ Keep on combing the hair for a longer time.

(5) Hair Treatment

1. Falling of hair Treatment :

➢ Clean the hair with shampoo. Then go for the hair treatment.

➢ Apply warm herbal oil all over the scalp in the partings of the hair with cotton.

➢ Massage for 20 to 25 minutes according to the steps of the oil massage.

➢ Allow the Ozone steam for 5 to 7 minutes after the massage.

➢ Give High Frequency current with the comb-electrode for 5 to 7 minutes in the wet hair.

➢ Mix the protein pack in the curd and apply it. Retain it in the hair for 45 minutes. Then wash out the pack.

➢ This treatment can be done at the interval of 10 to 15 days.

2. Dandruff Treatment :

➢ Wash the hair.

➢ Mix anti-dandruff lotion in the herbal oil. Apply it in the partings with cotton.

➢ Massage according to the oil massage steps for 10 to 15 minutes.

➢ Allow the Ozone steam for 5 to 7 minutes.

➢ Allow strong High Frequency current in wet hair for 7 to 10 minutes.

➢ Mix two teaspoonful of the protein pack in extra sour curd and apply it in the hair. Let it retain for 45 minutes.

➢ Shampoo the hair.

3. Split-ends Treatment :

Split-ends means a hair ending in two splits. Such hair prevents the hair growth and makes the hair look rough. Therefore, it is very important to cut the split-ends. This treatment can be done only in dry hair. Take a strand of hair twist it and hold it between two fingers. Run your fingers along the strand till its end. Then cut the double ends with the scissors or burn it with a live candle. To avoid the split-ends, massage the hair with warm oil. Get the hair trimmed at regular intervals. Besides this, hair-conditioning is advised. For hair-conditioning, *Mehandi*, hair-food or cream-conditioner (a product of some reputed company) is to be used. Dry hair should never be given a wash.

4. *Mehandi* (Heena) Conditioning :

Mehandi is an ancient herb. Man has used it for ages. The ancient Egyptian women used it. It is also called 'herbal dye'. Women are always worried about their greying hair as such hair makes them look older. The growth of grey hair cannot be prevented by picking it out. The white hair cannot be turned black in a natural way. The only remedy to change the colour is *Mehandi*. *Mehandi* is the best way of conditioning, colouring and nutritioning the hair. It makes the hair shine. It makes the hair smooth and soft. If *Mehandi* is to be applied in the hair, do it in dry hair and if at all conditioner is to be used, do it in oily hair.

* **Caretaking :**

● Never apply *Mehandi* without mixing *amla*, egg, etc., in it, otherwise it will give dryness to the hair.

* **Method of applying *Mehandi* :**

➢ Put the hair ear to ear. Take a thin strand of hair from the crown area, apply *Mehandi* on it, twist it into a tiny bun. Then take a thin strand from the rear. Apply *Mehandi* on it and go on setting one after another into buns in the opposite direction. Follow the same pattern for the front hair, too.

➢ Retain the *Mehandi* in hair for one hour. Make it a point that only white hair turns into red and never all the hair.

'Hair *Mehandi*' is used for conditioning.

Never use black *Mehandi* for the 'Hair *Mehandi*' because it has chemicals.

➢ In Hair *Mehandi* powder, mix boiled water of tea or coffee and soak it in plain water.

Mehandi is cool by nature, so it is applied on palms and hands and in the hair to cool down the body temperature.

Don't apply the *Mehandi* in the hair of children as far as possible.

Those who have chronic cold are advised not to retain *Mehandi* in the hair for a long time. After applying the *Mehandi*, such persons are supposed to take some hot drink like tea, coffee, etc..

(a) For dry hair : For two hours, keep soaking 200 grams of *Amla* powder, 100 grams of *Mehandi*, two teaspoonful of coffee, yolk of one egg, and one teaspoonful of curd. Then apply *Mehandi* following the method mentioned above and wash it off after retaining it for 40 to 45 minutes.

(b) For oily hair : For one hour, mix and keep soaking 100 grams of *Amla* powder, 100 grams of *Mehandi*, 2 teaspoonful of coffee, half a cup of curd, 4 to 5 drops of lemon juice and yolk of one egg. Apply *Mehandi* following the method suggested above and after retaining it for 40 to 45 minutes wash it off.

(c) For conditioning : For some time, keep soaking half a cup of curd, half a cup of *Amla* powder, 2 eggs and 2 to 4 drops of lemon juice in half a cup of *Mehandi*. Apply *Mehandi* as suggested previously. Retain it for 30 to 40 minutes and then wash it off.

5. Hair Food :

Hair food makes the hair shining, silky, colourful and healthy. It removes scalp-problems and diseases of hair. It also functions as conditioning for the hair. It prevents the falling of hair and functions as deep cleansing in scalp.

For hair food, mix in curd the powder of long-plum, soap berry, sandal, Indian pennywort, eclipta, fenugreek seeds, bitter neem leaves, rose-petals, orange-peel, jasmine flower and the juice of gourd. Two teaspoonful of *Mehandi* powder can also be mixed in this. This mixture is to be kept soaking for 2 to 3 hours before using. Following the method mentioned previously, retain the hair food for 45 minutes in the hair. Then wash the hair with plain water. After the hair is dry, do the oil massage in hair. Wash the hair with the shampoo the next day. The herbs in hair food turn more effective if the hair food is kept soaking for the said time. It is also called protein pack.

2. HAIRCUT

Haircut adds to the human personality. Haircut can be done in two ways :

Haircut

Horizontal	Vertical
* Straight-cut	* Step-cut
* 'U' Shape-cut	* Boy-cut
* 'V' Shape-cut	
* Blunt-cut	
* Sharp Blunt-cut	

*** Apparatus used for Haircut :**

➢ Sharp scissors for haircutting

➢ Haircutting Apron

➢ Setting clips

➢ Tail comb

➢ Water spray bottle

➢ Round and half brush

➢ Paddle brush

➢ Hair dryer

➢ Soft brush

*** Things to be taken care of while cutting hair :**

➢ Hair must be freshly washed before the haircut.

➢ Wet all the hair with the spray bottle and remove all the knots.

➢ Part the hair in thin strands according to the hair-growth and pin them up.

➢ After parting, the lowest part is to be cut off according to the required shape.

➢ Now, lower the pin-ups one by one and cut it according to the previously-set guideline.

➢ Don't cut the hair exactly in the measure as the customer has suggested, because after getting dry, the hair looks shorter than the exact measurement.

➢ After cutting the hair, blow it dry for the final look.

➢ Horizontal-cut looks more decent for straight hair while vertical-cut looks better for curly and wavy hair.

*** Pin-up of Haircut :**

At first, part the hair ear to ear from the middle and pin-up the partings. Take some hair below the crown area in round and pin it up. Make more partings of the hair as per the growth of the hair and pin-up them.

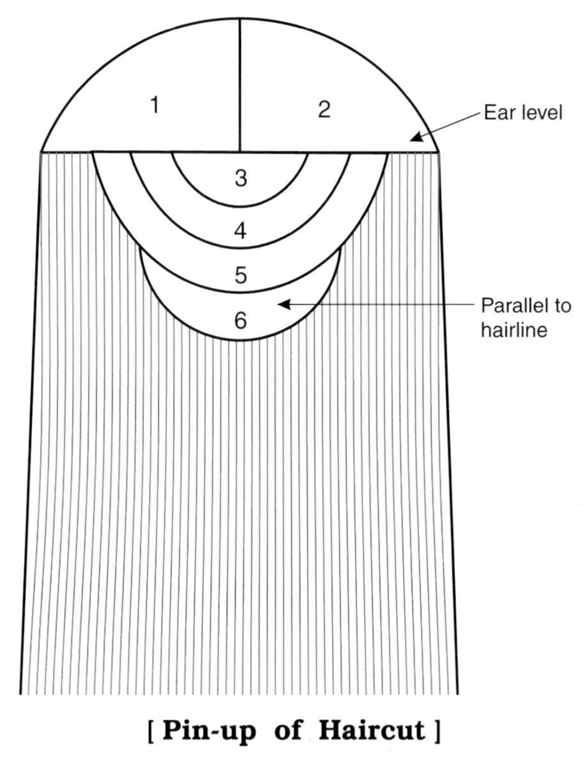

[Pin-up of Haircut]

(1) Types of Haircut

1. Straight Haircut
2. Round Shape Haircut
3. 'U' Shape Haircut
4. Deep 'U' Shape or 'V' Shape Haircut
5. Blunt Haircut
6. Step Haircut
7. Sharp Blunt Haircut
8. Boy Haircut
9. Layer Haircut
10. Feathers Shape Haircut
11. Mushroom Blunt Haircut
12. Baby-cut
13. Pot Shape Haircut
14. Innovative Haircut

* Techniques of Haircut :

- ➢ Notching
- ➢ Thinning
- ➢ Point cutting
- ➢ Slicing
- ➢ Flying
- ➢ Texturising
- ➢ Zig-zag cutting

* Degrees of Haircut :

(1)

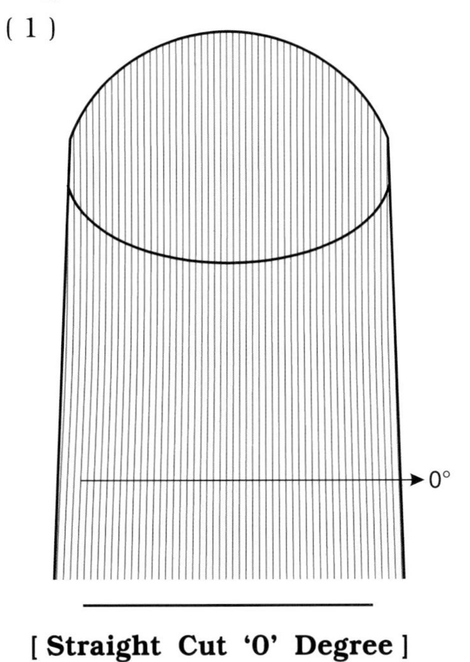

[Straight Cut '0' Degree]

(2)

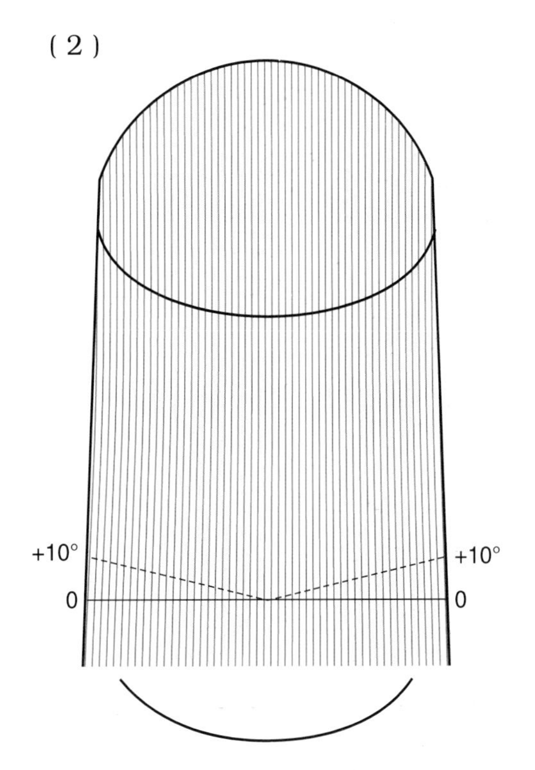

[Round Shape Cut '10' Degree]

(3)

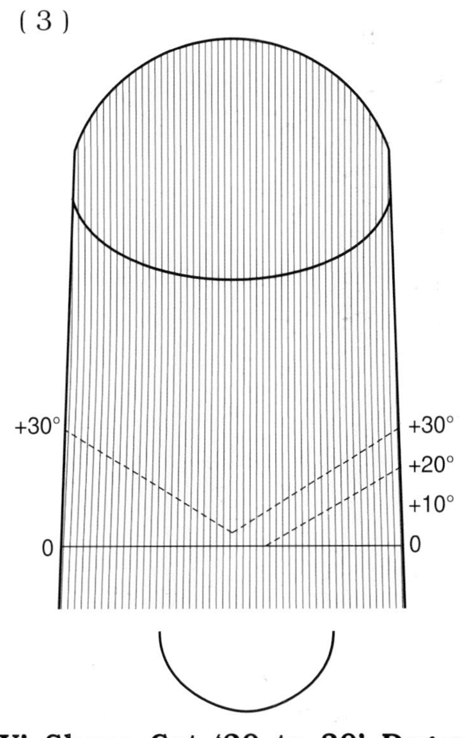

['U' Shape Cut '20 to 30' Degree]

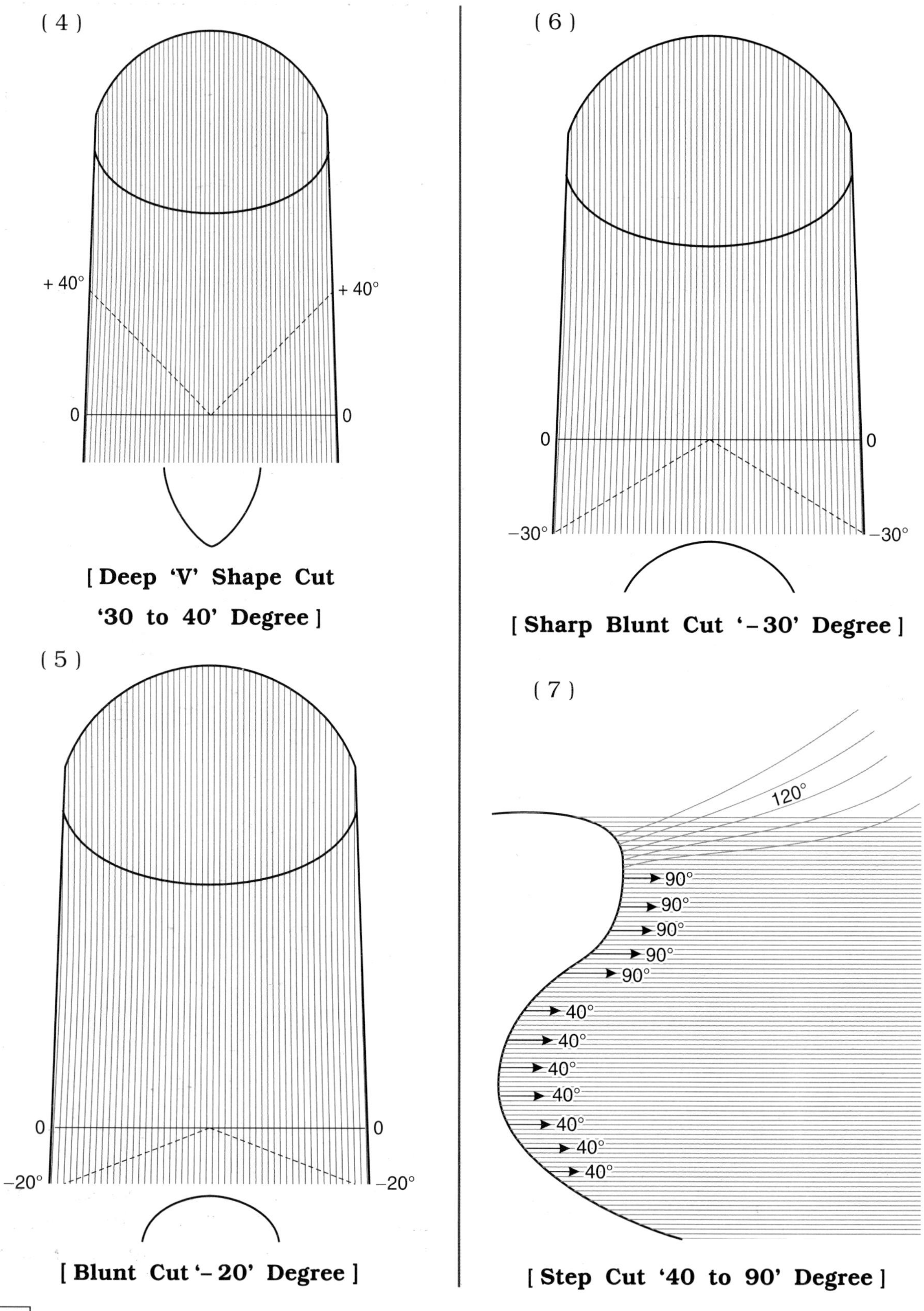
(4)
+ 40°
+ 40°
0
0
[Deep 'V' Shape Cut
'30 to 40' Degree]
(6)
0
0
−30°
−30°
[Sharp Blunt Cut '– 30' Degree]
(5)
0
0
−20°
−20°
[Blunt Cut '– 20' Degree]
(7)
120°
90°
90°
90°
90°
90°
40°
40°
40°
40°
40°
40°
40°
[Step Cut '40 to 90' Degree]

1. Straight Haircut :

[**Straight Haircut**]

Part the hair as per the growth and make it straight at 0°. Then take down the pin-ups one by one and cut them straight at 0°. Then taking position exactly behind the client, bring the front hair back and cut it straight.

2. Round Shape Haircut :

Part the hair properly and cut the hairline at 0°. Then bring the upper parting down. Cut it at 20°. Thus, bring down all the partings one by one and cut each of them at 20°.

Cut the middle part at 0°. Then take the side hair on one side and cut it at 20°.

[**Round Shape Haircut**]

3. 'U' Shape Haircut :

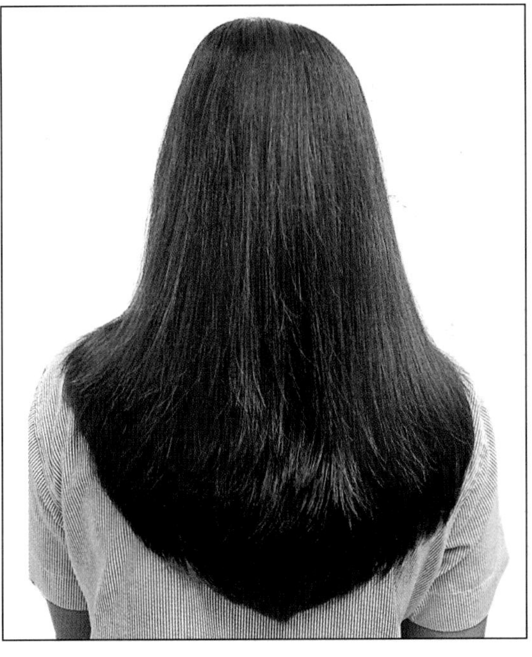

[**'U' Shape Haircut**]

Part the hair properly and cut the hairline at 0°.

Then bring the upper parting down, and cut it at 30°. Thus, take down all the partings one by one and cut them at 30°.

4. Deep 'U' Shape or 'V' Shape Haircut :

[Deep 'U' Shape or 'V' Shape Haircut]

Part the hair properly and cut the middle hair at 0°. Now, hold the scissors-points upwards and cut the side hair at 40°. In this cut, front hair is short and back hair is long. For the deep-cut of the front hair, cut it at 50° to 60°.

5. Blunt Haircut :

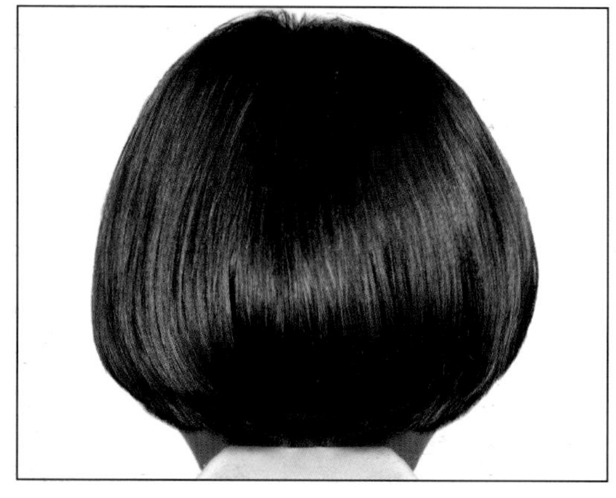

[Blunt Haircut]

Part the hair properly, cut the hair in the middle at 0°. Bring the front hair back, give it straight-cut and point-cut the hair. Keep its length up to the 'neckline'. This length can be made short or long as required. If the length goes down the shoulders, it won't lend the blunt effect.

6. Step Haircut :

[Step Haircut]

Step Haircut is a vertical-cut. At first, pin-up the hair in 6 partings. Cut the hairline in the 'U' shape-cut or in the deep 'U' shape-cut. Then take down the parting No. 6. Take the guideline of the hairline and cut it at 45°. In the same way, take down the parting No. 5 and cut it at 45°. Then take down partings – 4 and 3 and cut them at 90°. If 4 to 5 steps are to be done, cut the partings – 4 and 3 at 120°. Now from the front, cut the hair at the level of eyebrows, nose, lips, chin or chest in layers at 45°.

If boy haircut is to be done, it can be done in the same way as above and make it short taking the guideline of the neck-level.

7. Sharp Blunt Haircut :

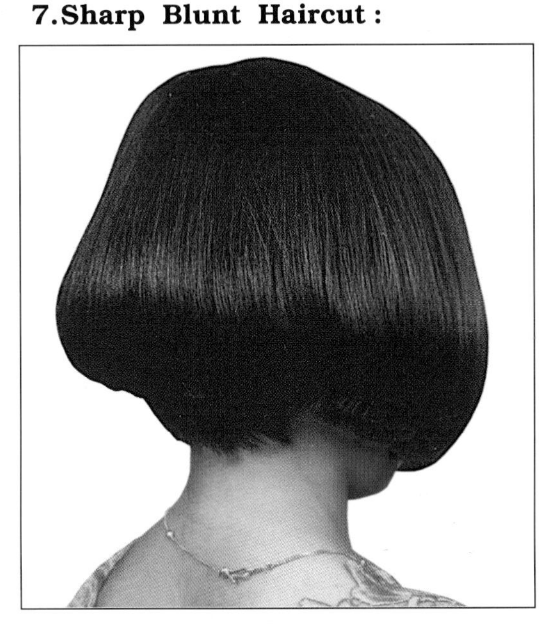

[Sharp Blunt Haircut]

Part the hair and cut the middle hair at 0°. Then cut the side hair with the scissors-points down at 20° to 30°. In this cut, the side hair looks longer.

8. Boy Haircut :

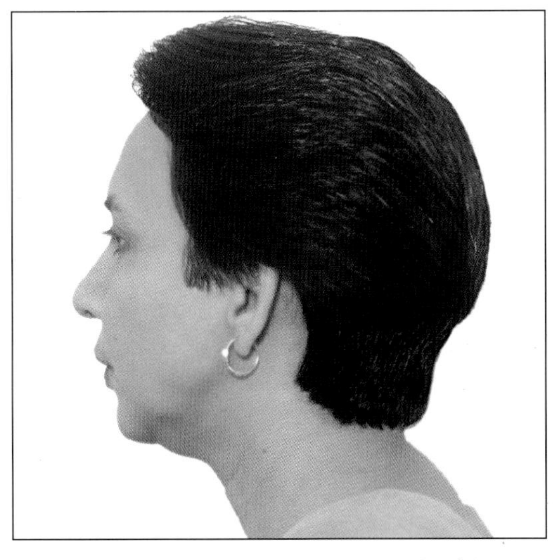

[Boy Haircut – Side View]

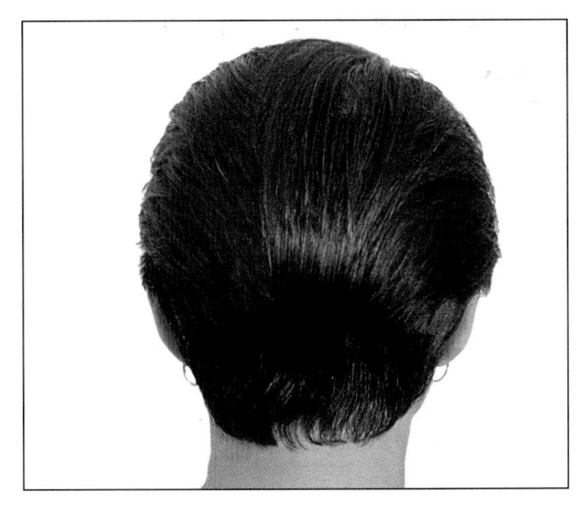

[Boy Haircut – Back View]

For this pin-up, as suggested on page No. 46 cut the lower hair at 0° in the round shape. Take down the pin-up Nos. 6 and 5 and cut them at 45°. Cut the pin-up Nos. 4 and 3 at 90°. Bring the front hair (Pin-up Nos. 1 and 2) near ears, take the guideline of back hair and cut it at 0°. Make parts and cut them at 45° and 90°.

9. Layer Haircut :

[Layer Haircut]

In this cut, the hair is very short in the front and very long at the back. This cut is to be done keeping one's position in the front of the client. Take the hair ear to ear and cut the middle hair up to chin level at 0°. Then take thin strands of hair from sides, keep the scissors-points downwards and make layers by point-cutting. Bring the back hair in the front and match it with the guideline. In an inch of lower hair-ends, allow the cut with notching or texturising scissors. The texturising can be done with a razor, too. If short hair is required, shorten it at the eyebrows-level, at the nose-level or at the lips-level.

10. Feathers Shape Haircut :

[Feathers Shape Haircut]

In this cut, there is very short hair in the front and very long hair at the back. Take the hair ear to ear and cut the middle hair up to the chin level at 0°. Take the thin strands of the side hair, keep the scissors-points downwards and make layers with point-cutting. Bring the backhair to the front and match it with the guideline. Allow 1 to 5 inch flying, cutting or notching in the front hair, so that feathers, effect can be obtained.

11. Mushroom Blunt Haircut :

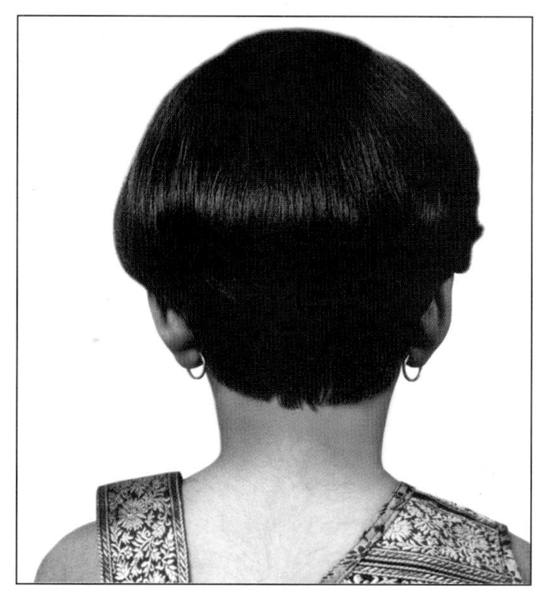

[Mushroom Blunt Haircut]

Mushroom Blunt Haircut is the combination of the Horizontal type of Haircut as well as the Vertical type of Haircut. Pin-up the hair as in the Boy-cut hair style. Raise the lower hair and cut it at 0°. Comb the hairline and cut it allowing point cut. Take down the pin-up Nos. 5 and 6 and allow straight cut like blunt cut from the apex-level. Take down the pin-up Nos. 3 and 4 and match them taking the guideline of Nos. 5 and 6. Bring the front hair pin-up Nos. 1 and 2 to the back and match it with the guideline. After this cutting, allow the cut at 45° to the top hair.

12. Baby-cut :

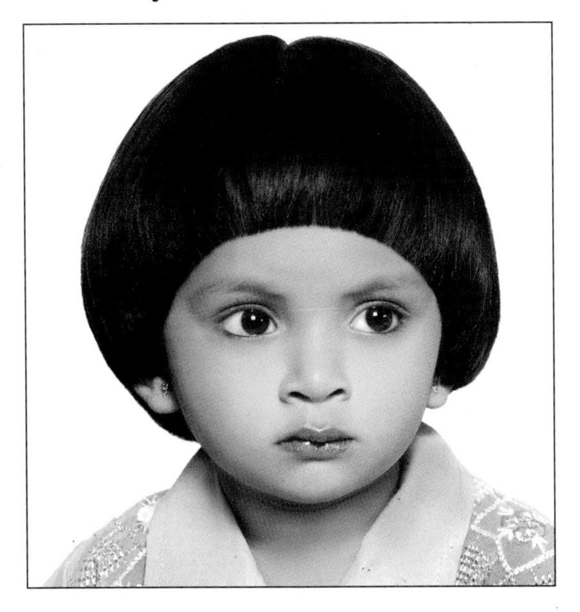

[**Baby-cut – Front View**]

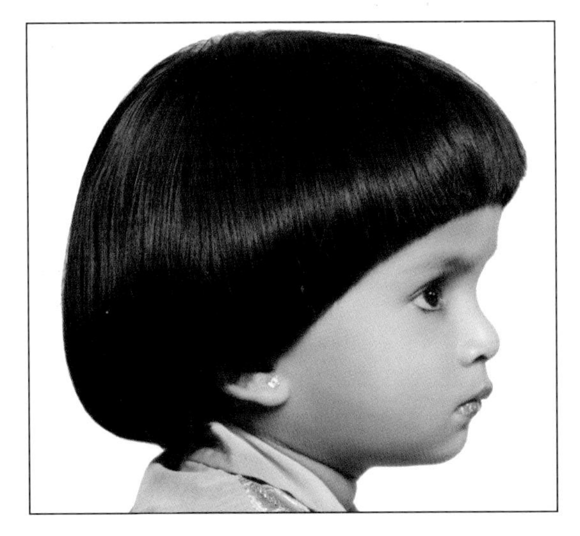

[**Baby-cut – Side View**]

This cut is preferred mostly by very young girls. According to the pin-up No. 6 as suggested on page No. 46, cut the lower level at 0°. Take down the pin-up and match it with the guideline. Set the front hair in the triangular shape. Then, point-cut it at 0°, a little above the eyebrows.

13. Pot Shape Haircut :

[**Pot Shape Haircut – Front View**]

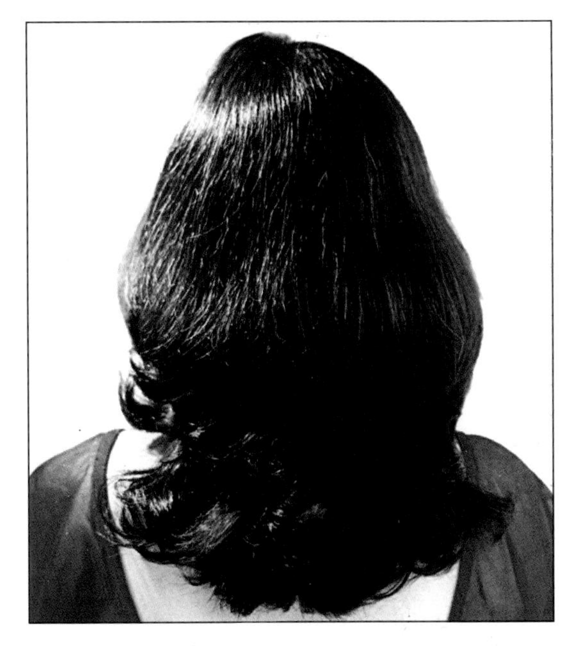

[**Pot Shape Haircut – Back View**]

Allow the box-parting up to the crown area from the middle of the eyebrows. Leave the hair at the cut of 180°. Give 'U' or 'V' shape to the lower hair. Match it with the top-cut and allow step-cut.

14. Innovative Haircut :

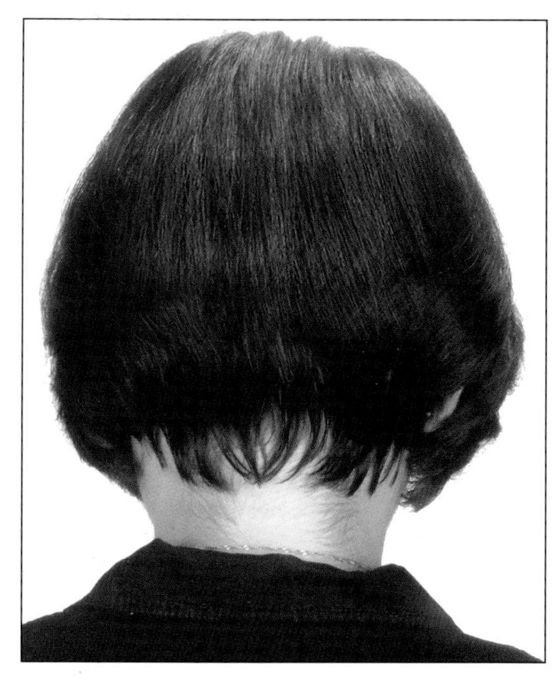

[Short Hair – Innovative View]

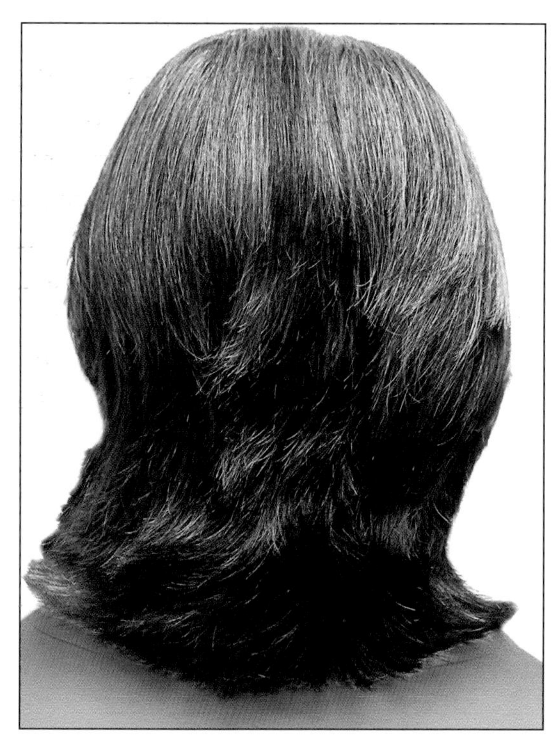

[Mid-length Hair – Innovative View]

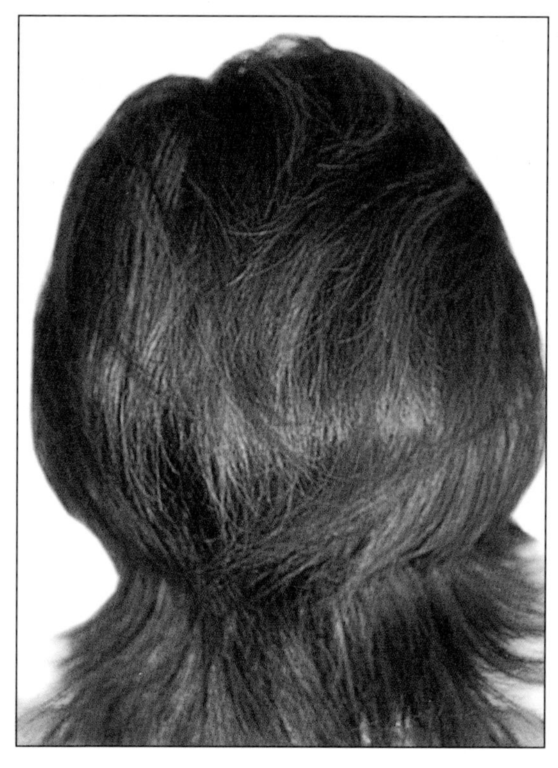

[Long Hair – Innovative View]

This cut can be done along with any cut to allow volume in the crown area. With this cut, the person looks tall. It gives pyramid like look in the crown area.

(2) Hair Setting

1.Blow-dry Hair Setting :

Blow-dry means setting the hair in the cut-style after the haircut. Blow-dry can be done speedily in less time.

2.Inturn Hair Setting :

Before hair setting, the hair should be made wet. Apply gel or mousse in hair. With the application of gel or mousse, the hair shines and the hair-set retains longer. Pin-up hair after applying gel or mousse. After the pin-up, turn the lower hair with a round brush. After one pin-up (5 and 6), take down another two from the upper level one by one and by allowing the drier, inturn them with the round brush. By doing this, the hair will get volume and retain longer.

3.Outturn Hair Setting :

[Outturn Hair Setting]

Pin-up hair as suggested on page No. 46. Then bring the pin-ups down one by one and set them outturn with a thin brush. To make the outturn hair-set longer, spray the hair a little before starting the hair-set. For the outturn hair-set, set plastic rolls in a hood dryer and keep it there for about an hour. Outturn hair-set can also be done with even an electric rod.

4. Roller Hair Setting :

[Roller Hair Setting]

Pin-up as suggested on page No. 46. For the roller hair setting, hot rollers, plastic roll, rubber spiral roll, etc., can be taken help of. Set the hot rollers outside. In the ear to ear parting, go for thin pin-ups and set the rollers. After keeping up the rollers for one hour, they can be taken out. If the hair is more silky, it can be kept in a hood dryer, too.

5. Ironing Hair Setting :

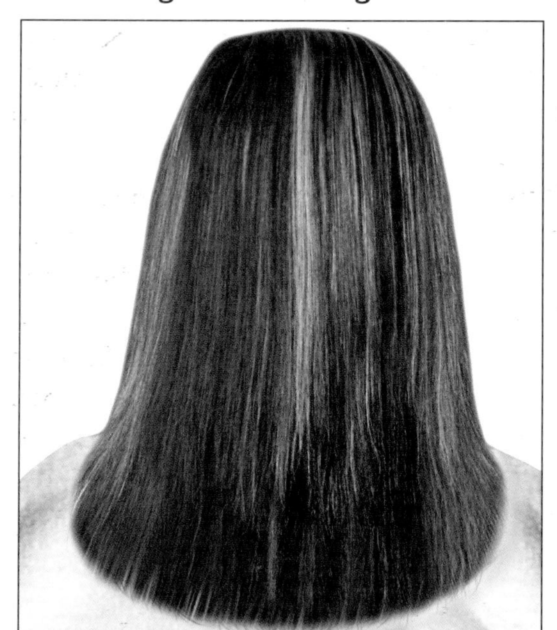

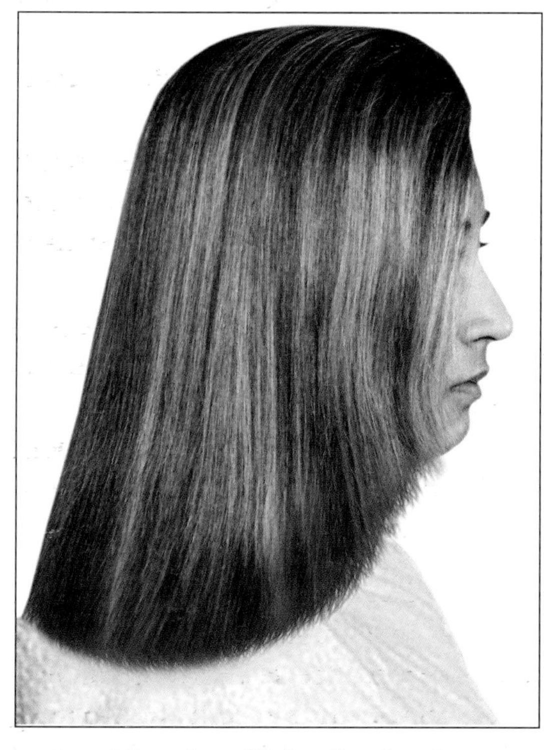

[Ironing Hair Setting]

Ironing means straightening hair temporarily. Even curly or wavy hair can also be straightened, of course, temporarily. Before ironing, wash the hair with the straightening shampoo conditioner. Then towel-dry the hair, apply ironing serum and pin it up. Blow-dry the hair with the paddle brush. Once more pin-up the hair in thin strands. Then iron it with the ironing machine. Ceramic iron will bring in better result. The ironing effect retains till the hair is not made wet again.

6. Crimping or Netlook Hair Setting :

[Crimping Hair Setting]

Pin-up hair as suggested on page No. 46. Straighten the hair allowing blow dry. Then pin it up once more and crimp the hair, pressing it in the crimping machine. This is how crimping is done in hair. If 'Netlook' is to be done, follow the same process and keep the hair in the 'Netlook' machine.

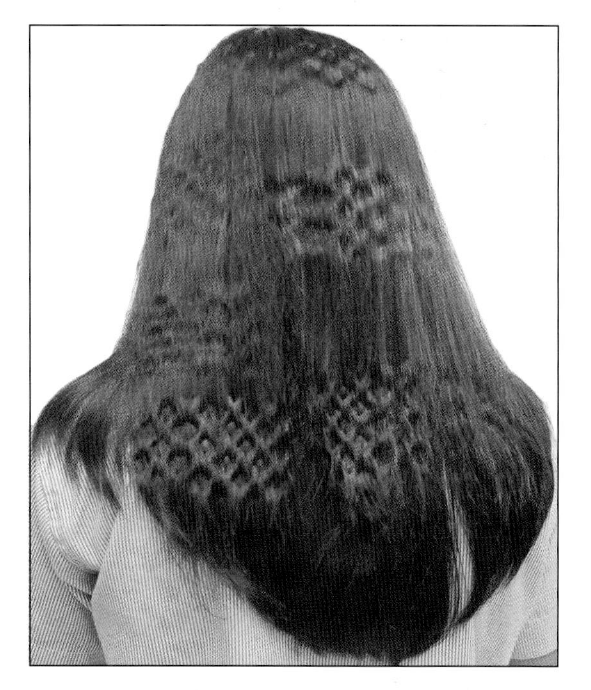

[Netlook Hair Setting]

(3) Hair Dye

Dyeing is colouring the hair (mostly brown or black). It is a chemical dye. Sometimes, on certain skin, a dye can cause reaction, too. For the testing, apply a little of the dye in some part behind the ear. If the reaction is felt, avoid using such dye.

*** There are three types of Chemical Dyes :**

➢ Powder dye
➢ Cream dye
➢ Liquid dye

*** Apparatus used for Dyeing :**

➢ Glass bowl or Plastic bowl
➢ Gloves
➢ Comb
➢ Dye brush
➢ Hair cap
➢ Apron, Self-apron
➢ Dye remover
➢ Cotton

*** Method of Dyeing Hair :**

Wash the hair with shampoo and get it dried thoroughly. Mix the chemicals for the hair dye as has been instructed on the hair dye packet. Part the hair in thin strands and apply the dye. Take care that the dye does not get on to the skin. If there is a stain on the skin, wipe it off with the dye remover. Retain the dye in the hair for the specific time as is suggested on the dye packet. Then wash it out and use the conditioner. It is very much required to use conditioner after washing out the dye, especially for the regular users.

*** Taking Care while Dyeing :**

➢ Don't mix dye in any metal container / pot.

➢ Hair must not be sticky. It must be dry.

➢ If it is liquid dye, cork the bottle tightly and keep it away from direct light; otherwise the dye will get oxydized and hence be useless.

➢ The day on which the hair dye is planned, wash the hair with shampoo and don't use the conditioner.

➢ Use up the mixed dye soon. Don't let it keep exposed for a longer time or for future use.

(4) Hair Perming

Perming is a method of making hair curly or wavy. The less growth of hair can be shown more growth by perming the hair. Perming adds to the beauty of face and helps lend a different look to personality. There should not be any coating on the hair like that of dye, *mehandi*, hair-pack, etc., while perming. Because of any such coating, perming cannot be done. Perming is not advised for very sensitive or chemically processed hair. Perming rolls are of different size. The selection of perming rolls depends upon the selection of curls. If vertical waves are required, the perming rolls like vertical sticks are to be used. It is called spiral perm.

∗ Apparatus and Material used for Perming :

- ➢ Clarifying shampoo
- ➢ Plastic bowl
- ➢ Cotton
- ➢ Tail comb
- ➢ Perming roll
- ➢ Tissue paper
- ➢ Perming lotion
- ➢ Neutralizer
- ➢ Apron
- ➢ Perming cap or Shower cap

∗ Pin-up for Perming Rolls :

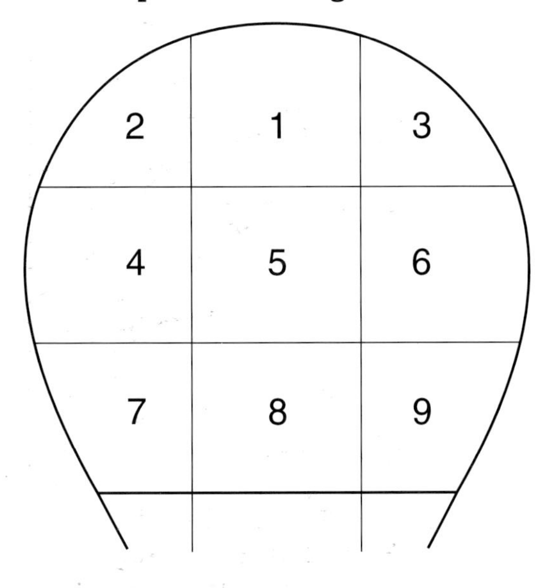

[Pin-up for Perming]

∗ Method of Perming :

➢ Wash the hair with clarifying shampoo and towel-dry it. So the hair would be perfectly clean.

➢ Then pin-up as shown in the above picture.

➢ Take thin sections of hair, put tissue paper on the edge of the hair and set the rolls in outturn or inturn. If larger curls are expected, use thick rolls.

➢ Wind the rolls as the style of perming one chooses.

➢ Take all the pin-ups one by one and set the rolls taking thin sections of the hair.

➢ After setting all the rolls, hold one by one roll in hand and apply perming lotion with the nozzle-bottle.

➢ Attach the perming cap or the shower cap and close all the rolls. It will help create heat that facilitates creating waves in the hair.

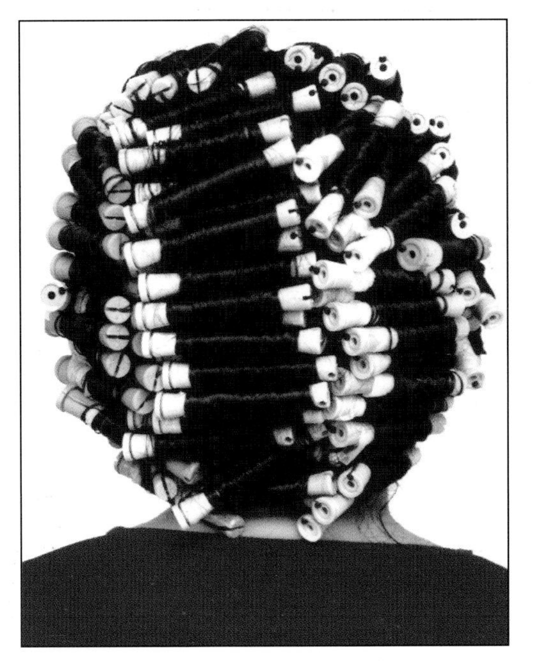

[Hair with Perming Rolls]

➢ Set the roll according to the instruction on the lotion that you use. Take off the shower cap and check one roll. If the waves are found as per your expectation, unfold the rolls. If the expected waves are not found, keep the rolls in the hood dryer for some more time.

➢ Clean off the lotion with water without unfolding the rolls and dry the hair with the napkin and the tissue paper.

➢ Hold each of the rolls in hand and apply neutralizer on it. Retain the neutralizer for five to ten minutes. Neutralizer helps retain the hair waves.

➢ Wash off the neutralizer with water without unfolding the rolls. Then wipe out the rolls with a napkin.

➢ Take off the rolls one by one properly. Then wash out the hair with water again. Wipe out the hair with the napkin lightly. Don't comb through the hair.

➢ Finally, apply the wet-look gel or the mousse. Don't shampoo the hair till two days after the perming.

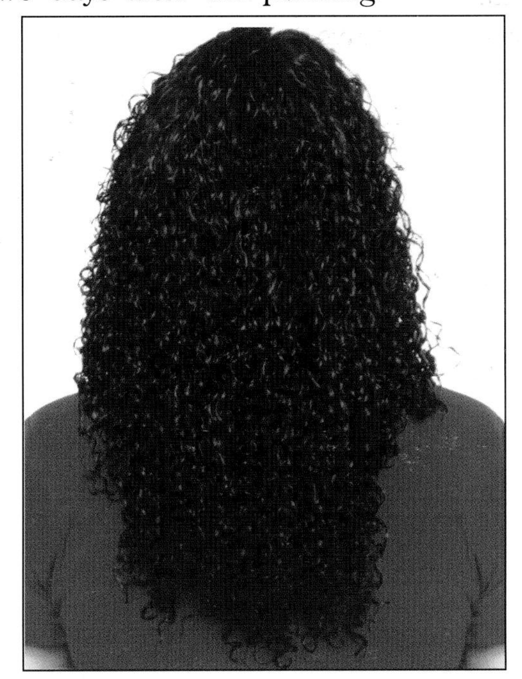

[Hair after unfolding Perming rolls – Back View]

[Hair after unfolding Perming rolls – Side View]

* **Caretaking :** • Take care that perming lotion does not reach the scalp.

• It is very important to use the protective shampoo and the conditioner.

• Retain the rolls in the hair till the time suggested on the perming-lotion product. If the rolls are kept longer, hair is supposed to get damaged because of the over-process.

(5) Hair Straightening

Straightening is the method to make the naturally wavy hair straight :

1. Temporary Straightening and
2. Permanent Straightening.

Temporary Straightening is also called ironing. It retains till one wash. In the Permanent Straightening, the newly growing hair keeps up their original growth.

There are three bonds in hair. For the Permanent Straightening, all these three bonds, are to be broken. For breaking these bonds, the chemical – 'Thioglycolic Acid' is used. This chemical is kept in a straightening tube. For the straightening, straightening cream and neutralizer are used.

* **Apparatus and Materials used in hair straightening :**

➢ Straightening cream and neutralizer

➢ Plastic bowl

➢ Brush

➢ Straightening board

➢ Ironing machine (Ceramic Iron)

➢ Gloves

➢ Paddle brush

➢ Dryer ➢ Apron

* **Method of Straightening Hair :**

➢ Wash the hair with the clarifying shampoo before straightening. Don't use the conditioner.

➢ Dry the hair with the napkin. If the hair is more curly, blow-dry thin hair with the paddle brush or do the light ironing with the ironing machine.

➢ Part the hair ear to ear in the front and do two partings from the crown area at the back.

➢ If the hair is dry, damaged or chemically processed, apply a protective product before applying the straightening cream.

➢ Take thin sections from the neck area and apply the straightening cream. Set the hair properly on the straightening board after applying the straightening cream.

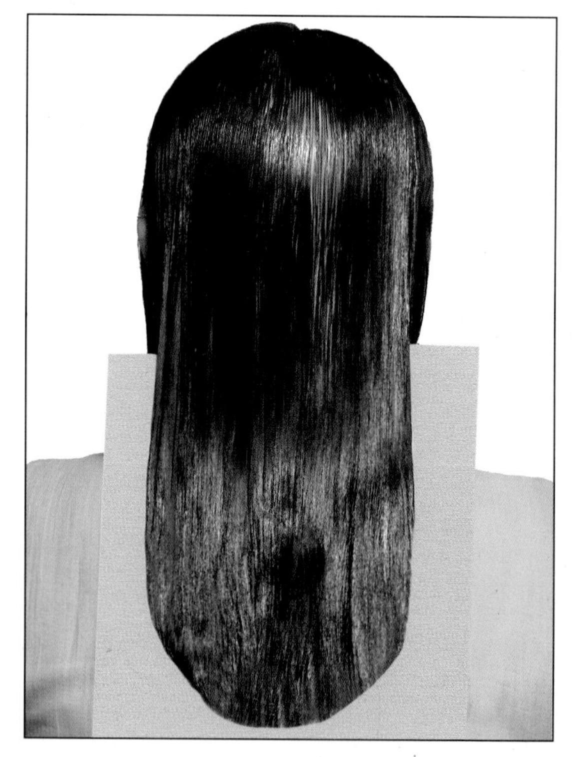

[Hair after applying Straightening cream]

[Hair on board after applying Straightening cream]

➢ Use the straightening cream according to the instructions on the straightening cream product of your choice.

➢ Then wash the hair. Take care not to pull the hair. See that the straightening cream is thoroughly washed out of the hair.

➢ Towel-dry the hair after the wash. Then blow-dry the hair with the drier and the paddle brush. Take thin sections of the hair and do ironing. The ironing should be done properly.

➢ After the ironing, apply the neutralizer in the same way as the straightening cream has been applied, and retain it for the time as instructed on the product.

➢ Wash out the neutralizer with water. Then wash it with the straightening control mask. This mask helps control straightening, makes it long-lasting and allows extra halt to the straightening.

➢ After doing the towel-dry, apply the straightening product. Then blow-dry the hair. Don't wash the hair for two days. Don't place the hair behind ears and don't tie it with rubber bands either.

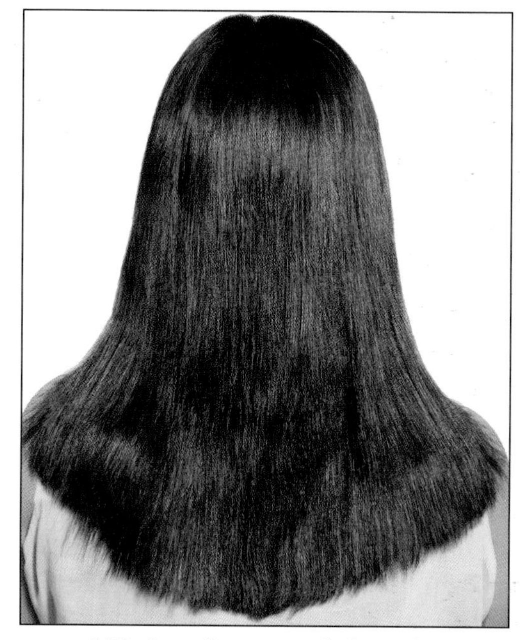

[Hair after straightening]

* **Caretaking :** • Take care that the straightening cream does not touch the scalp, because it has harmful side-effects.

• Retain the straightening cream in the hair till the time period suggested on the straightening product-box. Don't over-process it.

• Take help of an experienced and expert beautician for the straightening.

• Use the straightening product of a reputed company.

• Comb and maintain the hair according to the instruction by a beautician.

• After the straightening, use the straightening shampoo and conditioner for the regular wash.

(6) Hair Colour

The colour of hair is natural. To make hair look natural for ever, researchers have experimented and found out professional colours with the help of technology. Hair colour adds to the personality. Hair colour is done taking into consideration the person's profession, hair quality, skin type and appearance. Hair colour helps to do lightening in the hair. The lightening is done in two ways :

1. Natural Lightening and
2. Artificial Lightening.

➢ Natural Lightening is done by exposing hair to sunrays. It takes 6 months to 5 years. But it damages the hair.

➢ Artificial Lightening is done by ammonia. It opens the hair-cuticles and the oxygen in the developer lighten the hair. The colour in the tube colours the cortex which has turned pigment light. It could be clearly visible. This colour is permanent.

➢ Blue, red and yellow are primary colours. With their help, secondary colours can be developed. Ash, violet, red, gold, copper, mahogany, green, chestnut, etc., are secondary colours. There are base colours and colour reflect colour-pigment in the colour tube. With its help, hair can be coloured as required. This is professional colour range. There are many shades in it.

➢ Chemicals like ammonia, neutriciride, antioxidants, hydrogen and buffer are used in the hair colour tube. Ammonia is an alkaline agent. It opens the cuticles and gives colour to the hair. Colour tube is cream-based. It makes hair smooth and since it is in the cream form, it spreads easily. In the hair colour, another chief agent with tube is developer. It has hydrogen + oxygen in it. It is available in different quantities, i.e., 10 volume, 20 volume, 30 volume and 40 volume. In this developer, the oxygen potentiality is subsequently 3%, 6%, 9% and 15%. It helps making the colour light.

*** Base Shades of Hair Colour :**

➢ Black
➢ Dark Brown
➢ Darkest Brown
➢ Brown
➢ Light Brown
➢ Dark Blonde
➢ Blonde
➢ Light Blonde
➢ Very light Blonde
➢ Very very light Blonde

*** Two Methods of Hair Colour :**

1. Global Colour : Global colour means colouring all the hair fully. Global colour is done for white hair or for lightening or darkening the natural colour of hair. The global colour can be done in the matching with the natural colour or a little lighter than that. The global colour depends on the skin-tone and the growth of white hair. For the global colour 20 / 30 volume (6% to 9%) developer is used.

*** Ideal Mixing of Global Colour :**

75 ml developer in 1 (one) tube

40 ml developer in $\frac{1}{2}$ tube

20 ml developer in $\frac{1}{4}$ tube

∗ Method of doing Global Colour : Virgin Hair Technique

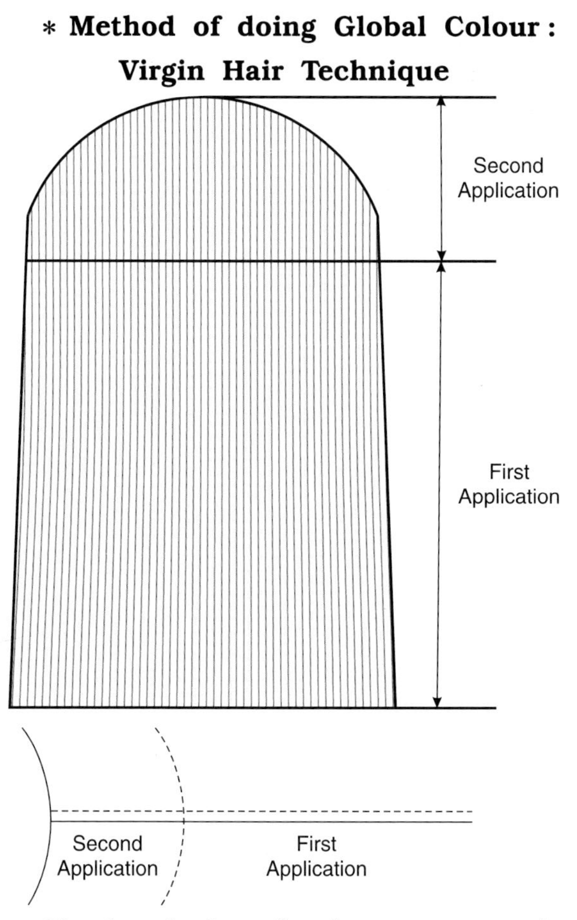

Check whether the hair is properly washed or not before doing the hair colour. Then part the hair ear to ear and make two parts of the back hair. Then apply the colour in about 1 to 1.5 inch area in one part. Massage the colour with fingers while applying it. In the same way, take thin sections of the hair and apply the colour all through the hair. This is how the first application is done. Then soon go for the second application for the same 1 to 1.5 inch part of the lower hair. Do it with 20 volume. Retain the colour for 35 to 40 minutes and then wash the hair. Use the special hair wash shampoo and conditioner only after the colour is completely removed from hair.

For full hair colour, (fashion-shade) take 20 to 30 volume developer for the application.

2.Highlights : The colour-process of making the natural hair colour lighter is called highlights. In 30% to 50% hair, this light-colouring is done in different ways.

Highlights can be done with honey, blonde, almond, copper, cinnamon, red, magenta red, copper red, ash blonde, silver blonde, platinum blonde, gray iceberg, milky pearly blonde, etc., colours.

Red highlights is done with 6% to 9% developer. Blonde highlights are done with 9% to 12% developer.

∗ Ideal Mixing of Highlights :

1 (one) tube + 100 ml developer (40 volume)

$\frac{1}{2}$ (half) tube + 50 ml developer (40 volume)

$\frac{1}{4}$ (quarter) tube + 25 ml developer (40 volume)

∗ Different Techniques of Highlights :

(1) Box Technique (2) Traditional Technique (3) Diagonal Technique

∗ Method of applying Highlights :

Highlights can be done with different techniques. It is done sparing 0.5 to 1 inch. Highlights depend more on skin colour. Aluminium foil is used for highlights. With the help of the aluminium foil, heat is created and it develops colour. Hair is tightly wrapped in aluminium foil so that the outside air does not get in and affect it. The developing time of highlights is 30 to 50 minutes. Highlights is done by slicing technique and weaving technique.

[**Blonde Highlights**]

[**Copper Red Highlights**]

[**Copper Highlights**]

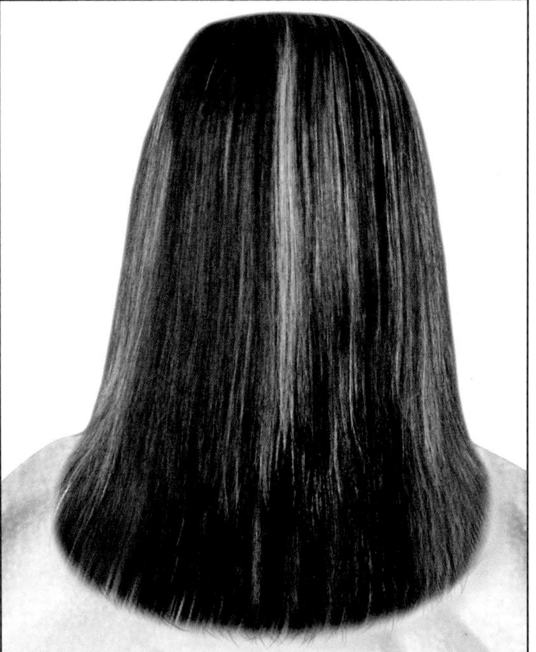

[**Global Blonde Highlights**]

SECTION 5 : MEHANDI & TATTOOS

1. MEHANDI

Mehandi is an important beauty cosmetic. *Mehandi* is essential for the fair sex on any good or auspicious occasion. Therefore, it holds the same ground as beauty treatment, hairstyle and make-up.

(1) Method of Applying *Mehandi*

➢ Dry *Mehandi* leaves and grind them into fine powder. *Mehandi* powder is readily available in the market, too. Filter this powder with a fine cloth twice to thrice.

➢ Put 8 to 10 drops of eucalyptus oil in the filtered lemon juice. Mix the fine powder of *Mehandi* in it as required. Keep it soaking for two hours and prepare the paste. **OR**

➢ Boil water with tamarind and tea-leaves. Then filter the water. Mix *Mehandi* powder in it as required. Keep it soaking for two hours and prepare the paste.

➢ Use a thin stick or a plastic cone for applying this paste. For applying *Mehandi*, plastic sticks, sandalwood sticks and ivory sticks are readily available in the market. Even the point of a needle will also serve the purpose.

➢ Keep the mixture of the lemon juice and sugar ready in one cup. After applying the *Mehandi*, apply this mixture with a cotton pad slowly on the parts where *Mehandi* is applied. Then go on applying the *Mehandi* to other parts.

➢ Retain the applied *Mehandi* till 4 to 5 hours to dry. Then shake it off. Let water not touch that part or parts for at least 12 to 14 hours. This would help *Mehandi* darken the colour.

➢ After shaking off the dried *Mehandi*, apply mustard oil on it. **OR**

➢ Heat clove (4 to 5) powder on the baking pan and in the smoke, warm the *Mehandi*-applied parts.

(2) Method of Making *Mehandi* Cones

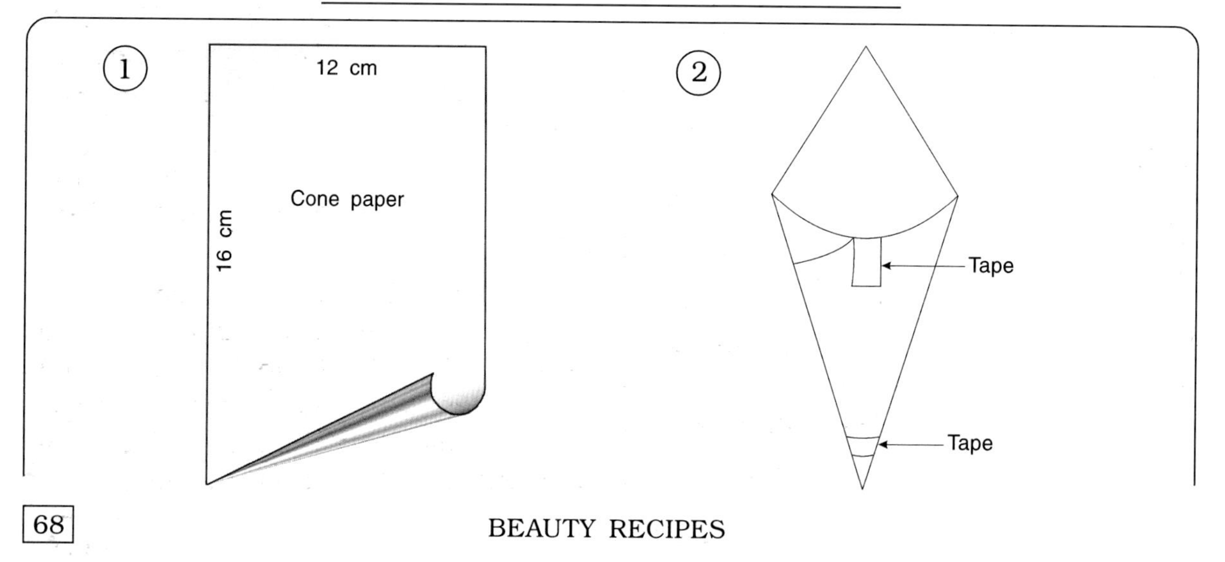

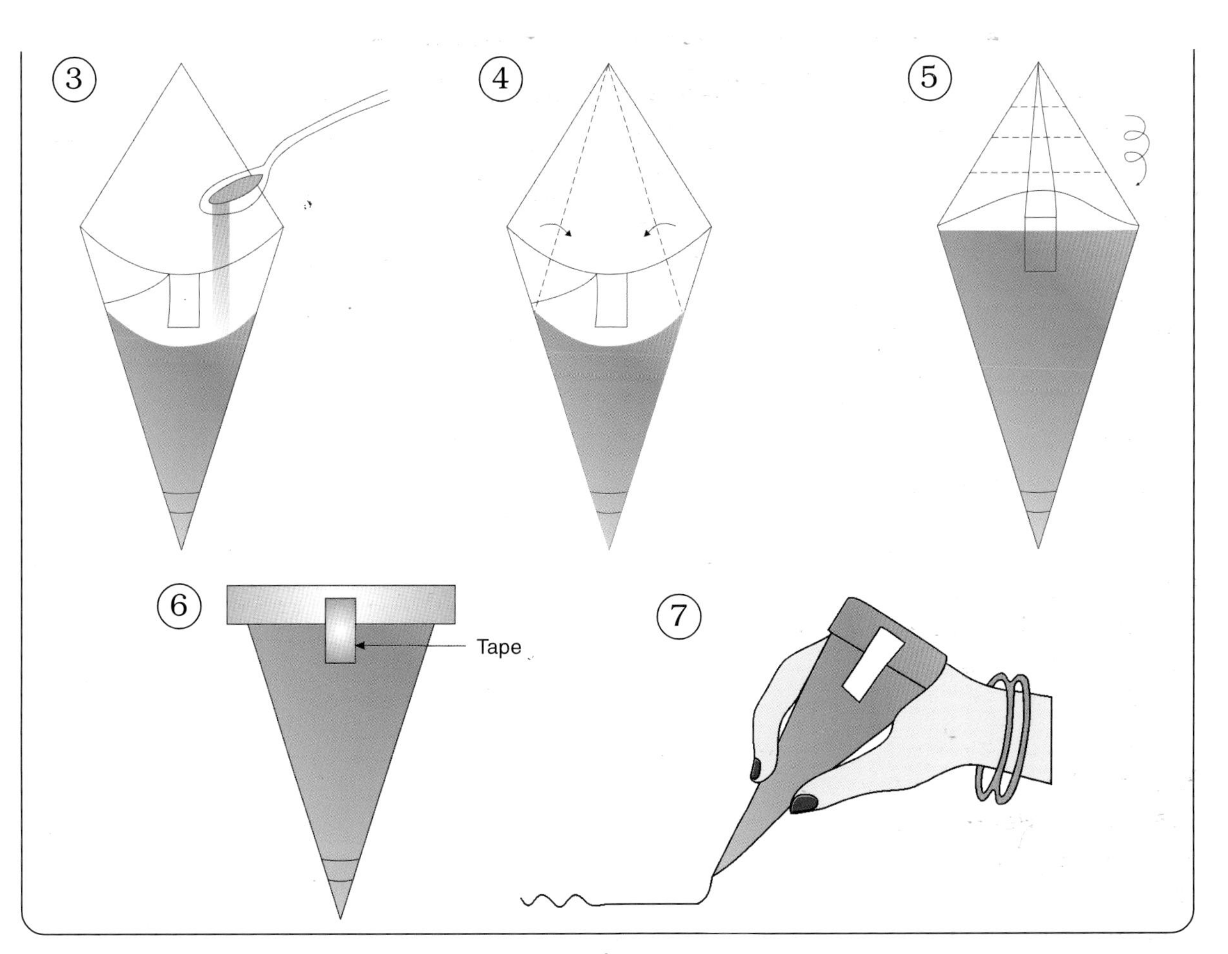

(3) Colourful *Mehandi*

➢ ***Jardosi (Jardoji) Mehandi* :** *Jardosi Mehandi* is done with a glitter. These glitters are readily available in the market. Another way : Mix glue in fine 'jari' powder, fill a cone with the mixture and apply the *Jardosi Mehandi*.

➢ **Black-Brown *Mehandi* :** Add water in black colour *Mehandi* powder, prepare the paste and the cone is ready for the application. Then make an outline with the black *Mehandi* cone and let it dry for 40 to 50 minutes. Wash the hands with water, dry them and fill in the gap within the outline with the cone.

➢ **Golden-Silver *Mehandi* :** This *Mehandi* is applied with golden and silver sparkle. This tube is easily available in the market. At first, design with silver sparkle. Then outline with golden sparkle. In the same way, the vice-versa can also be done.

➢ **Mirror work *Mehandi* :** Apply *Jardosi Mehandi*. Then, soon stick the small *jadtar* mirrors on the wet *Mehandi*.

In the same way *jadtar* stones can also be stuck to bring in the mirror-effect.

➢ **Nail-polish *Mehandi* :** Keep selected nail-polish bottle outside and allow it to be cool. Then fill it up in a cone and apply *Mehandi*. This *Mehandi* keeps stuck on hand for 5 hours and gives a different look then common ones.

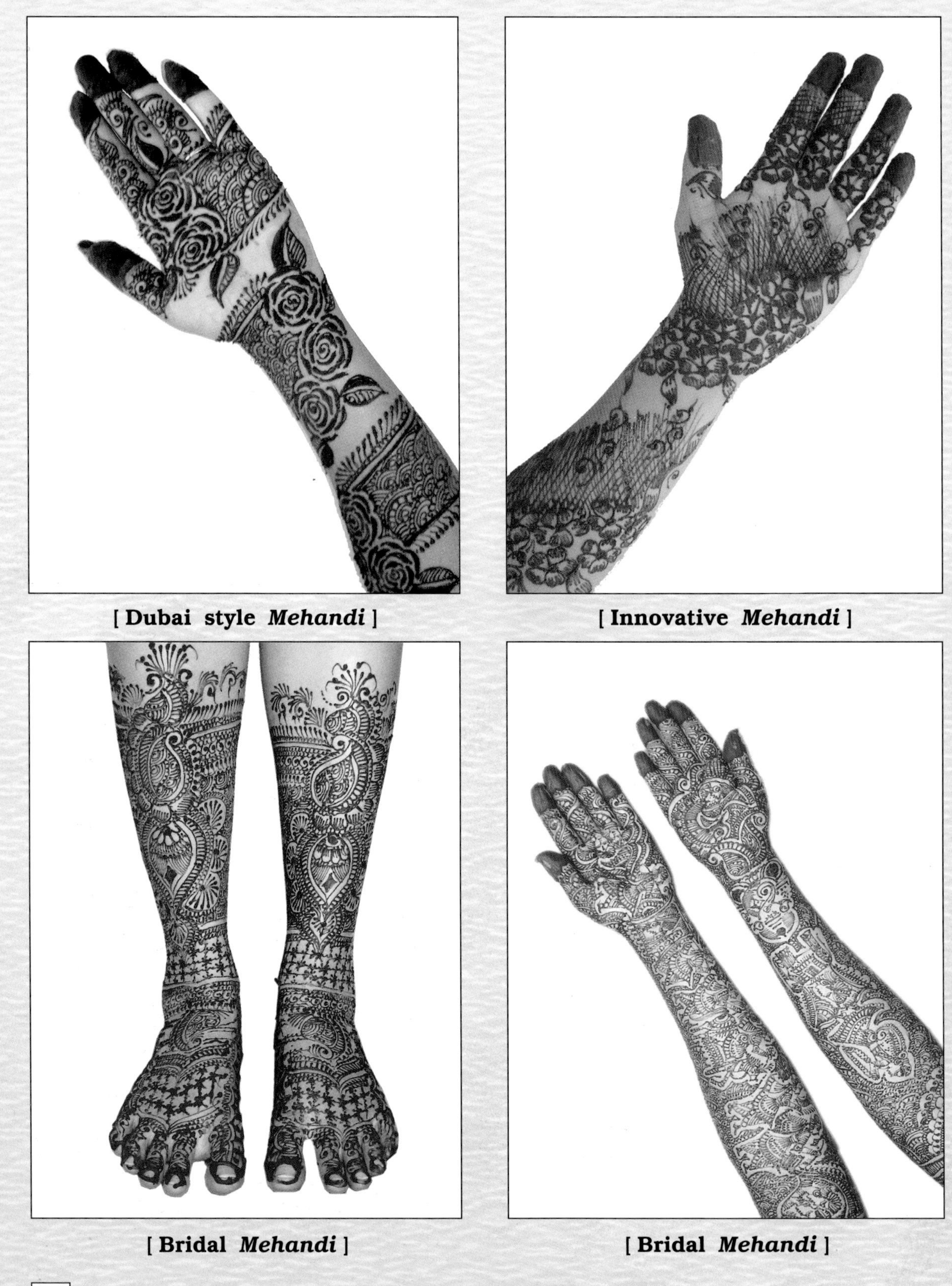

[Dubai style *Mehandi*]

[Innovative *Mehandi*]

[Bridal *Mehandi*]

[Bridal *Mehandi*]

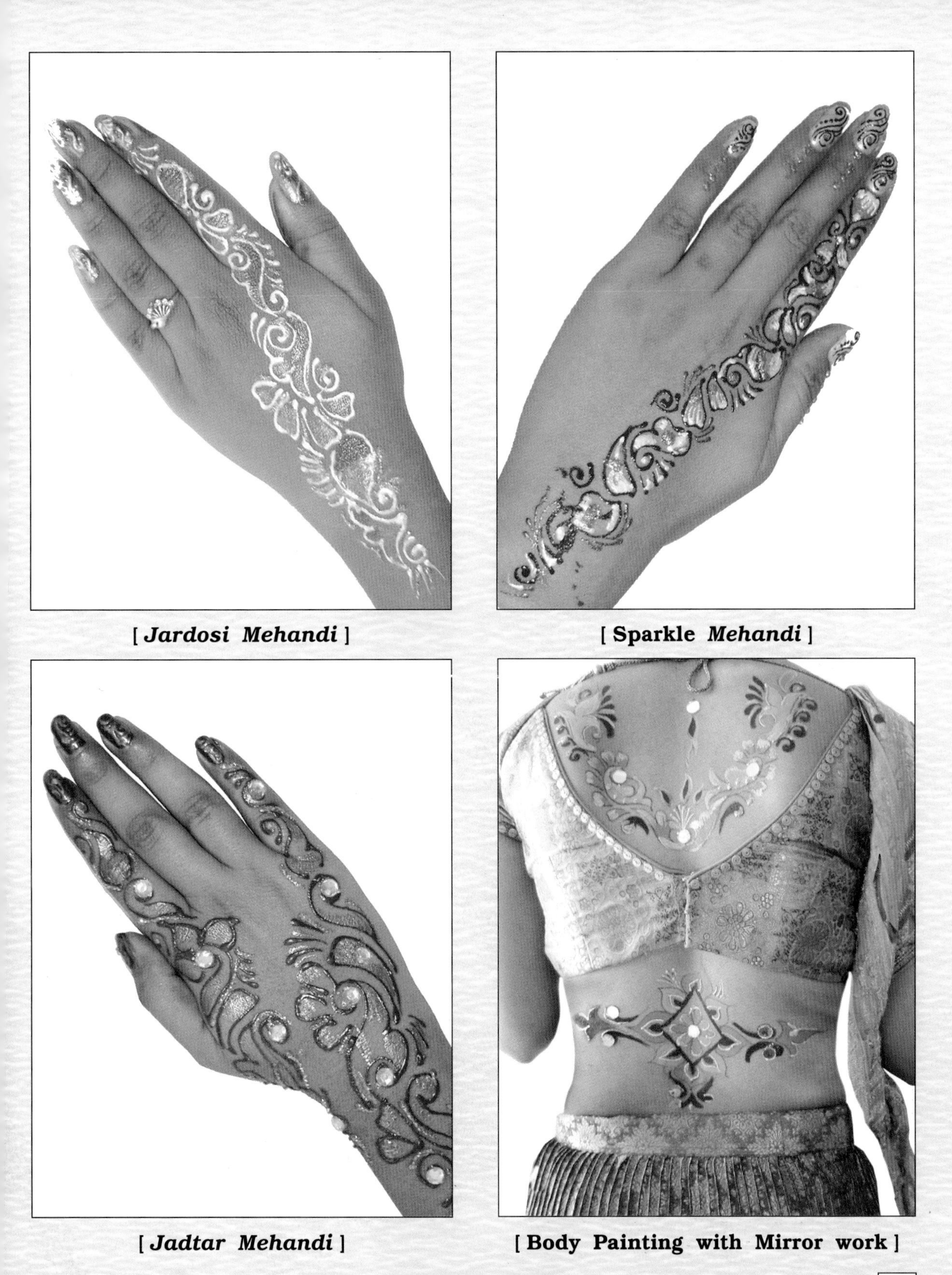

[*Jardosi Mehandi*]

[**Sparkle** ***Mehandi***]

[*Jadtar Mehandi*]

[**Body Painting with Mirror work**]

[**Zig-zag style *Mehandi***]

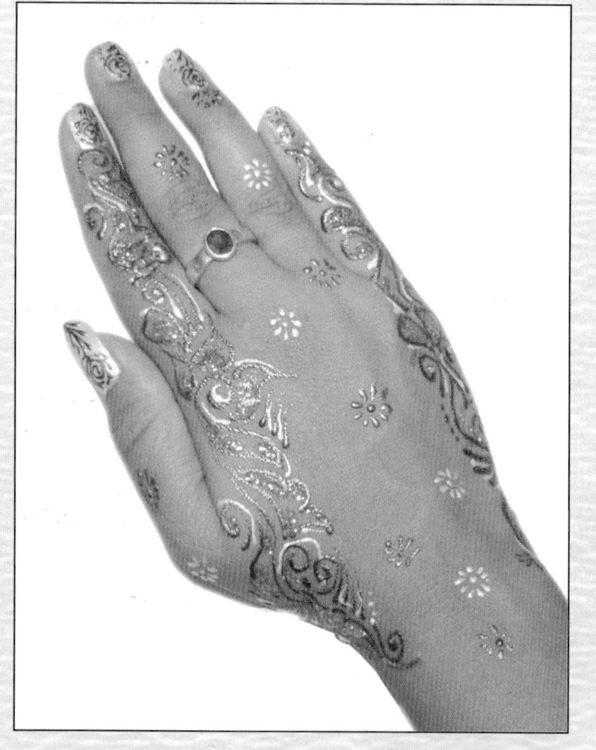

[**Innovative *Mehandi* with Nail Art**]

[**Innovative *Mehandi* with Nail Art**]

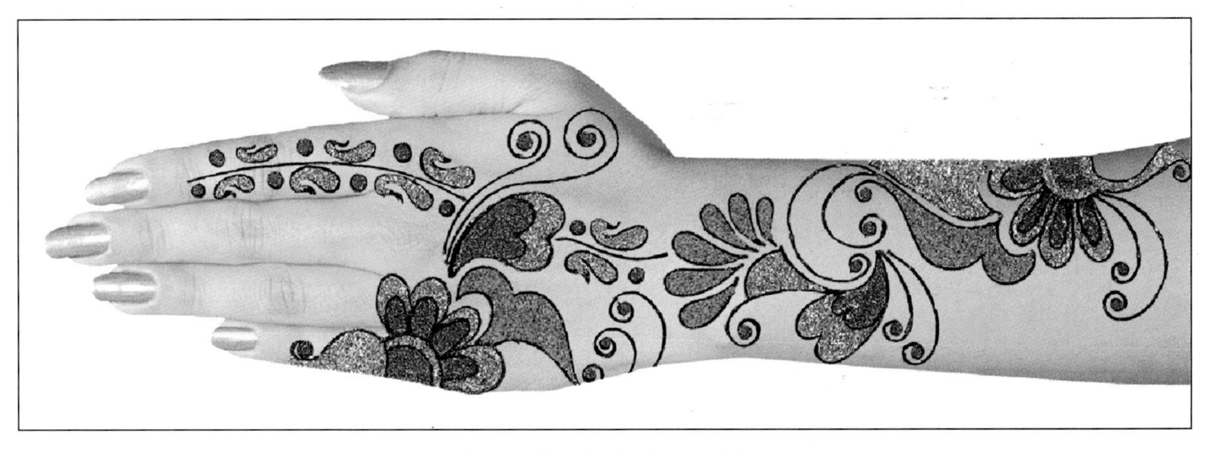

[*Jardosi Mehandi*]

(4) Tips for Applying *Mehandi*

➢ Wash the hands clean before applying *Mehandi*.

➢ Let the *Mehandi* dry out for at least 2 to 3 hours.

➢ Apply lemon juice and sugar mixture on the dried *Mehandi*.

➢ Peel off the dried *Mehandi* carefully. Don't allow water on that part for 24 hours.

➢ After peeling off the dried *Mehandi*, take the smoke of heated clove powder on the baking pan all over the part (palm). For darkening the colour more, apply balm on the palm.

➢ Don't allow soap on the hand so as not to let the *Mehandi* colour or tattoo fade away.

➢ Let the *Mehandi* get dry in its natural way. It takes a little more time in this way, so that its better effect can be had. In the airblow of an air conditioner, *Mehandi* gets dry sooner, therefore, better effect cannot be had.

➢ Nail-polish is to be had on nails well before you start applying *Mehandi*. It saves taking over the *Mehandi* colour on nails.

(5) Other Uses of *Mehandi*

The use of *Mehandi* is not restricted only to hands, feet and hair. The other uses of *Mehandi* are as follow :

➢ *Mehandi* functions as an astringent on the burns. It makes the burns heal.

➢ *Mehandi* is a proved antiseptic in Athlete's Foot and other cuts and wounds. It is also useful in headache, rashes and cuts. Gurgle boiled *Mehandi* water for throat sore or throat ache. If the temperature of body increases, *Mehandi* applied in the palms and soles brings the temperature down.

➢ For hair conditioning, *Mehandi* mixed with olive oil is applied.

➢ *Mehandi* is also applied in hair as conditioner every two weeks. It colours hair and prevents its falling. It also lessens the roughness of hair and brings in smoothness in hair.

➢ *Mehandi* is also used for nail-conditioning.

2. DIFFERENT TYPES OF BODY-TATTOOS

SECTION 6 : HAIRSTYLES

Various hairstyles are displayed (made) for parties, modelling sessions, marriages, ring ceremonies, etc.. Hair-style can be done in three stages as suggested below : (1) Holding (2) Moulding (3) Spreading

* **There are five types of hairstyle :**
  - ➢ Traditional Bun hairstyle
  - ➢ Western-Indowestern hairstyle
  - ➢ Braid hairstyle
  - ➢ Switch-fixing hairstyle
  - ➢ Loose hair hairstyle

* **Caretaking for Hairstyles :**

➢ Hair should not be oily for hairstyle.

➢ Consider the factors – face-cut, hair, view, profile, etc., while doing hair-style.

➢ Back-comb at 0°, 45°, 95°, 135° and 180° is done for hairstyle.

➢ Different hairsprays are used for different hairstyles :

- For loose hair hairstyle – Normal hairspray
- For front waves – Ultra hairspray
- For standing roll or tall style – Ultra hairspray
- For final hairstyle – Hard hairspray

➢ For the rough hair, perfect spray is used and for the loose hair, mousse or gel is used.

➢ If the hairspray is done closely, it brings about shine in the hair. If it is done from a little distance, it gives a matt-look and if it is done from considerable distance, it gives a velvet or funky-look.

(1) In-bun Hairstyle

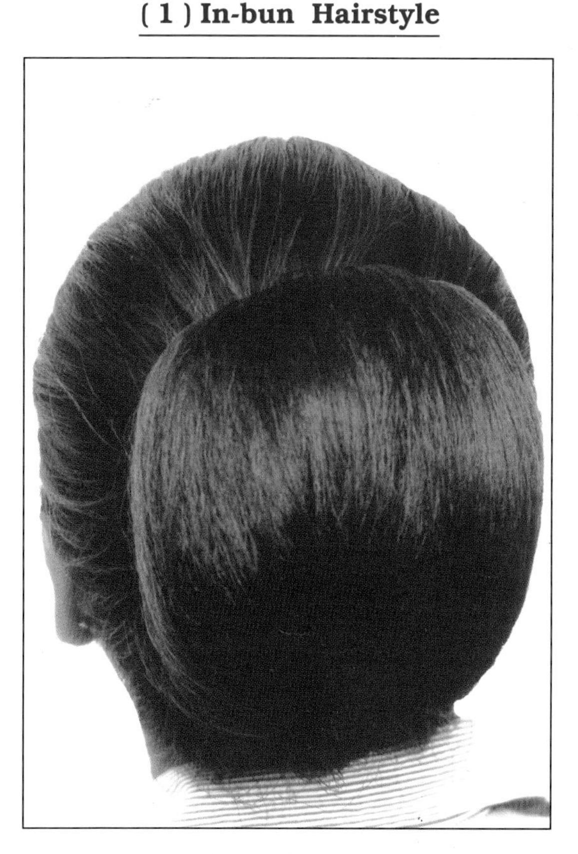

[In-bun Hairstyle]

At first, comb the hair properly and part the hair ear to ear. Take a very low ponytail of the back hair. Pin-up the ponytail from sides and spray it. Mould the ponytail inside, make its bun and pin it up inwards. Then spray-finish it. Take the puff of the ear to ear parted hair, according to the face or according to the choice of the customer. After the pin-up, twist the extra hair or make tiny rolls of it and set the rolls over the bun. Attach a matching broach. This hair in a twist, can be set around the bun in a circle.

(2) Low-bun Hairstyle

[Low-bun Hairstyle]

At first, part the hair ear to ear and take a very low ponytail of the back hair. Pin-up the ponytail from sides and spray it. Then take an additional bun. Twist the end of the ponytail inside or outside, tight it and fit it. Tie a net over it. Then take a proper puff of the front hair and pin it up. Roll the pin-up according to the growth of the hair or overlap them over the bun and pin them up. Then spray it and do finishing. Attach a matching broach to it.

(3) Chinese-bun Hairstyle

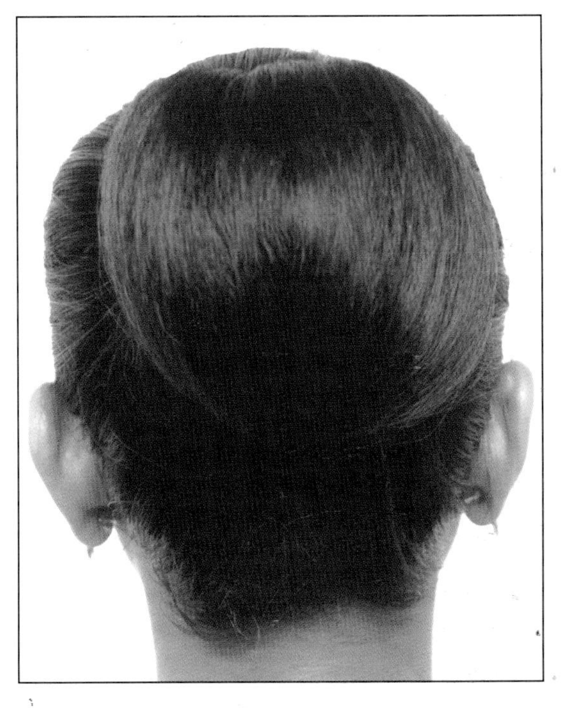

[Chinese-bun Hairstyle]

Part the hair ear to ear and make ponytail of the back hair on the crown area. Pin-up the front hair befitting to the face and put it with the ponytail. Then collect all the hair, roll it inwards, pin it up narrow from below and make a bun. Spread the bun-hair side ways, pin it up and spray it for finishing. Attach a matching broach to it.

(4) Japanese-bun Hairstyle

Part the hair ear to ear and make a ponytail of the back hair over the crown area. Pin-up the front hair properly and put it together with the ponytail. Then pin-up the ponytail below. Then roll the pony-hair as it shapes narrow upside and downside, make a bun and pin it up. Spread the bun-hair side ways, pin it up and spray it for finishing. Attach a matching broach.

(5) Two-in-One Roll Hairstyle

[Two-in-One Roll Hairstyle]

Part the hair ear to ear and make a ponytail of the back-hair in the middle. Then make the puff of the front hair befitting the face-cut and pin it up. Divide the ponytail into two. Now overlap the left part over the right part and pin it up as it looks two-in-one roll (two rolls from one). Make two to three rolls according to the growth. Back-comb the other part (right part), mould the roll out and set it beside it. Then attach a matching broach.

(6) Hill Hairstyle

Part the hair ear to ear and make a ponytail in the middle. Then make a proper puff of the front hair and pin it up. Mix the additional hair of the pin-up with the ponytail. Then part the ponytail into two. Make four to five parts of that one part according to the growth. Take the first part, mould an out-roll of it till the half of it and set it on the lower part. Then go on making rolls of the other extra parts and keep on setting them in a round on the lower part. Then make the finger rolls of the rest one part of the upper hair and set the rolls in a round on the higher side. Then attach a matching broach on one side.

(7) Dignity Roll Hairstyle

[Dignity Roll Hairstyle]

Part the hair ear to ear and make the ponytail of the back-hair in the middle. Then take a proper puff of the front hair and pin it up. Set the extra hair of the pin-up around the ponytail and pin it up. Divide the ponytail in three parts. Bring one part to the right side, make its roll and pin it up. Bring the other part to the left side, make its roll and pin it up. Make a roll of the third part in such a way that it looks as if one roll comes out of another and pin it up. Attach a matching broach.

(8) Cross Roll Hairstyle

Back-comb the front hair, make a puff of it and make a ponytail of the entire hair. Take the upper hair of the ponytail and make an out-roll over the ponytail. Take the right side hair of the ponytail, roll it, set it on the left side and pin it up. In the same way, take the hair on the left side of the ponytail, roll it up and set it on the right side. In this way, set the rolls in cross according to the growth of the hair. As one out-roll has been set over the pony, set an in-roll below. Spray-finish the hair and attach a matching broach to it.

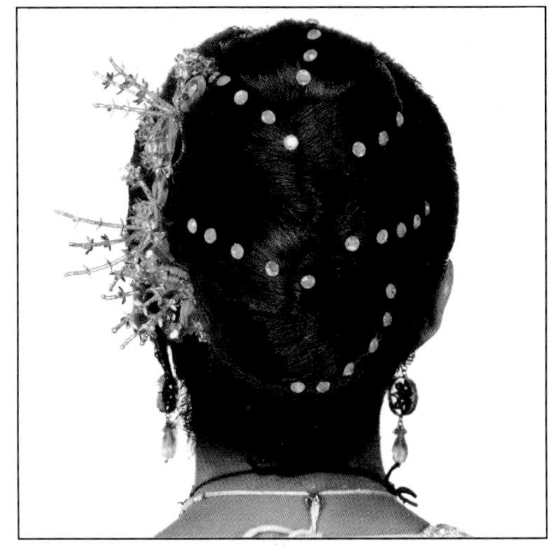

[Cross Roll Hairstyle]

(9) French Roll Hairstyle

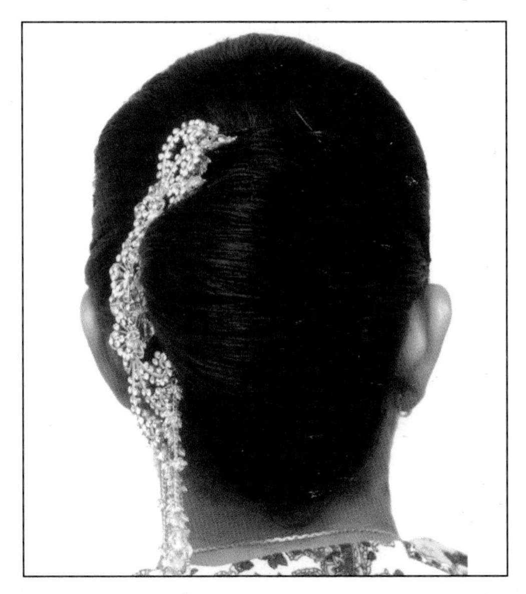

[French Roll Hairstyle]

Part the hair ear to ear and pin-up all the back-hair taking it on one side. Back-comb and spray the pinned-up hair. Make French roll of the sprayed hair. Make a puff of the front hair and pin-up the extra hair on the side of the French roll. Attach a matching broach on one side of the French roll.

(10) French Roll Hairstyle (in Long Hair)

[French Roll Hairstyle (in Long Hair)]

Part the hair ear to ear. Divide the back-hair in $\frac{3}{4}$ and $\frac{1}{4}$ parts. Make the braid or twist of the $\frac{3}{4}$ part. Set it in the round and pin it up. Wrap the net on it and fit it with forks. Back-comb the $\frac{1}{4}$ part of the hair. Comb the hair, overlap it on the net and pin it up. Then twist the remaining hair and pin it up. Pin-up the front hair properly. Make the in-roll or finger-roll of the extra remaining hair of the pin-up and set it on the French roll. Attach a matching broach on one side of the bun.

(11) French Hairstyle with Hanging Roll

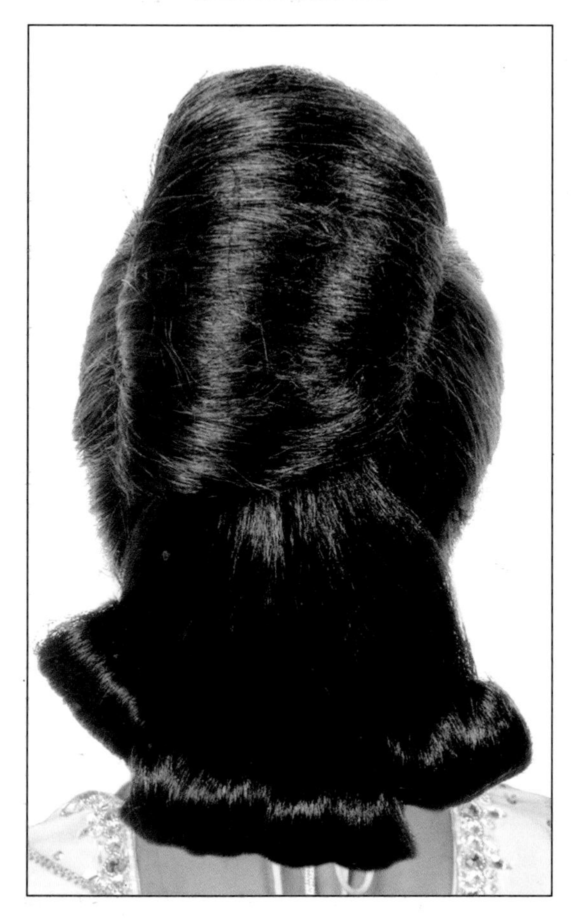

[French Hairstyle with Hanging Roll]

Part the hair ear to ear. Take the entire back-hair on one side and pin it up. Twist that hair, make a French roll of it and pin-up the remaining hair below the roll. Divide the hair into three to four parts of the hair below and make out-rolls of it. Then pin-up the front hair properly and overlap the remaining hair on the side of the French roll and pin it up. Attach a matching broach to it.

(12) Overlapping Hairstyle

[Overlapping Hairstyle]

Part the hair ear to ear. Take some hair of the crown area, twist it and set it in a circle. Pin-up the front hair properly and put together the remaining hair with the tiny bun. Divide the back-hair into two parts. Back-comb the hair of one side and overlap it on the twist. Then back-comb the hair of the other side and overlap it. If the hair is more, make one or two rolls and attach a matching broach to it.

(13) Funky-look Hairstyle

[Funky-look Hairstyle]

Part the hair ear to ear. Make pony-tail $\frac{3}{4}$ of the back-hair in the crown area. Pin-up the ponytail from either side and spray it. Pin-up the front hair and set it around the ponytail. Twist the ponytail and pin it up in the way that it keeps out 2 to 2.5 inches. Back-comb the $\frac{1}{4}$ part of the remaining hair and overlap it. Then put it together with the remaining 2 to 2.5 inch hair. Hard-spray the extra hair, back-comb it and lend it a funky-look. For more funky-look, once more back-comb the hair and hard-spray it. Attach a matching broach to it.

(14) Loose Hair Hairstyle (Pin-up with Outturn)

[Loose Hair Hairstyle (Pin-up with Outturn)]

Hairspray the hair. Then part the hair ear to ear. Pin it up as boy-cut hair in the back-hair. Then outcurl it with a hot rod. Thus, outcurl the entire lot of the hair. Pin-up the front hair. Outcurl the remaining hair and spray it. Then attach a matching broach to it.

Thus, crimping, spiral roll, netlook ironing, etc., are loose hairstyles. In each style a matching broach adds to the beauty.

(15) Hairstyles of Braid

[**Traditional Hairstyle**]

Part the hair ear to ear. Make a ponytail by taking half of the hair from the back-hair in a round. Run a string along the braid and fit it with the ponytail and knit the braid. Pin-up the front hair in the matching to the face. Set the remaining hair of the pin-up around the ponytail. Divide the lower back-hair in two parts. Overlap the left side hair after back-combing it and overlap the right side hair. Then pin it up. Fresh flowers or artificial matching broach can be attached round or along the length of the braid.

[**Funky-look Hairstyle**]

Part the hair ear to ear. Make ponytail of the entire lot of the back-hair. Tie up the funky-look braid with a black string to the ponytail. Set the remaining hair of the ponytail around the braid. Pin-up the front hair and set it around the braid. For the additional funky-look, set an additional funky-look frill upon the pin-up.

DIFFERENT HAIRSTYLES

[Funky-look]

[High-Roll]

[Highly Western]

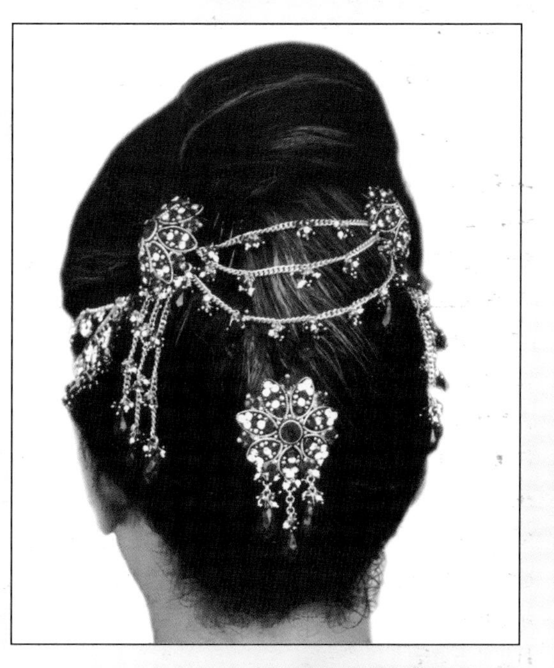

[Overlapping with In-Roll]

[Traditional Bun]

[Indowestern]

[Highly Western Bridal]

[Traditional Bun]

[Dignity Roll]

[French with Funky]

[In-Roll]

[Roller Setting]

SECTION 7 : MAKE-UP

Make-up plays a significant role in the present time. Make-up not only adds to beauty, but boosts up confidence, too. Make-up hides certain defects of the face.

Three things are essential to be checked before starting make-up : (1) Face Type (2) Skin Colour (3) Skin Concept

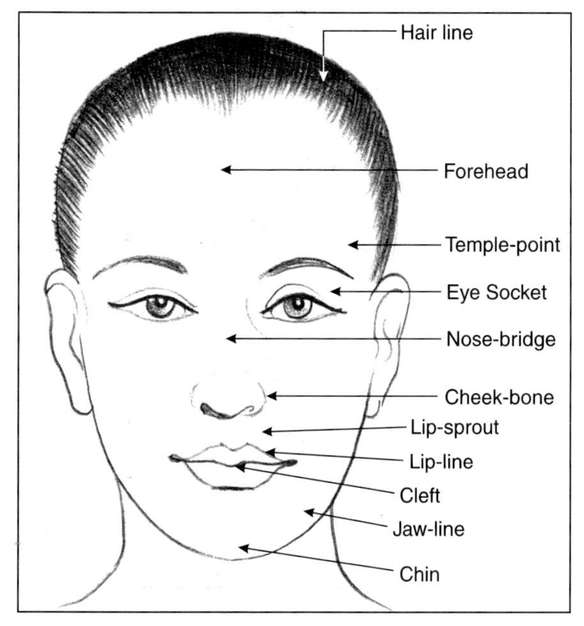

(1) Types of Faces

Generally, there are seven types of faces :

1. Round Face
2. Oval Face
3. Heart-shaped Face
4. Diamond Face
5. Square Face
6. Triangle Face
7. Long Face

Oval Face is considered to be the perfect face among all.

1. Round Face :

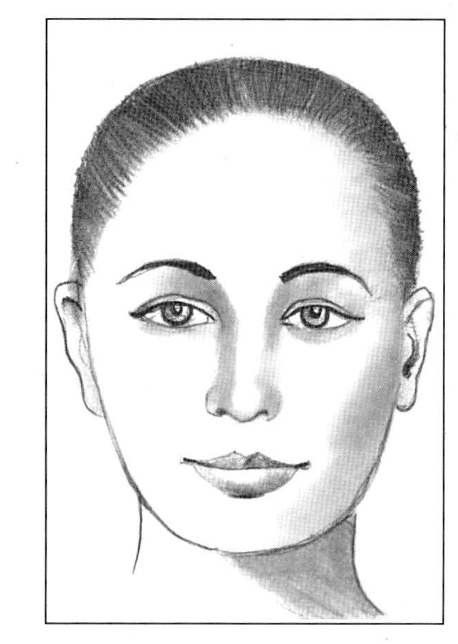

2. Oval Face :

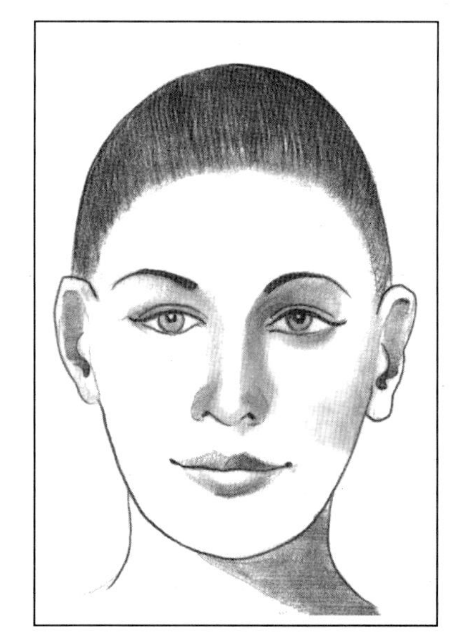

3. Heart-shaped Face :

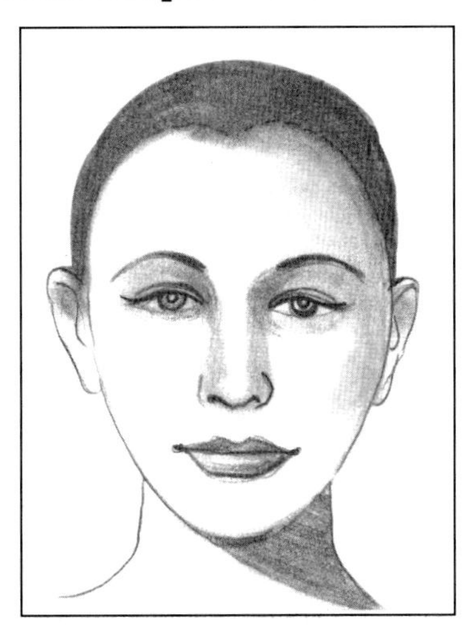

4. Diamond Face :

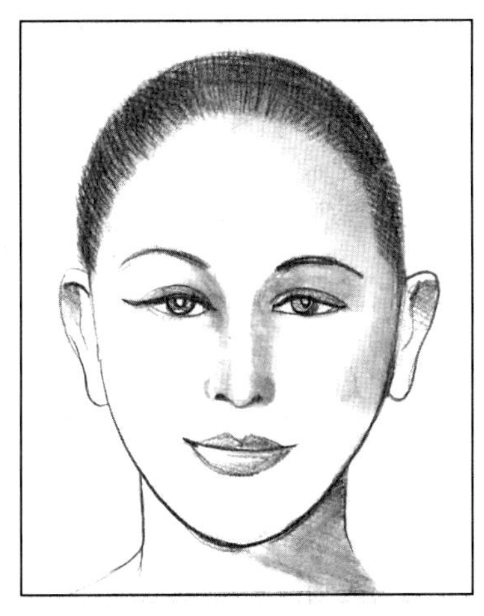

5. Square Face :

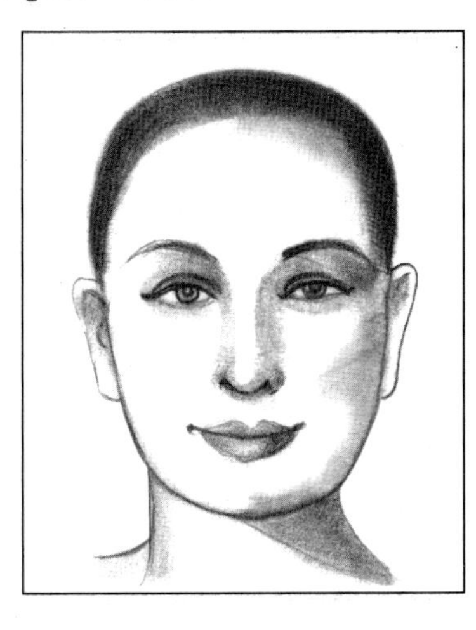

6. Triangle Face :

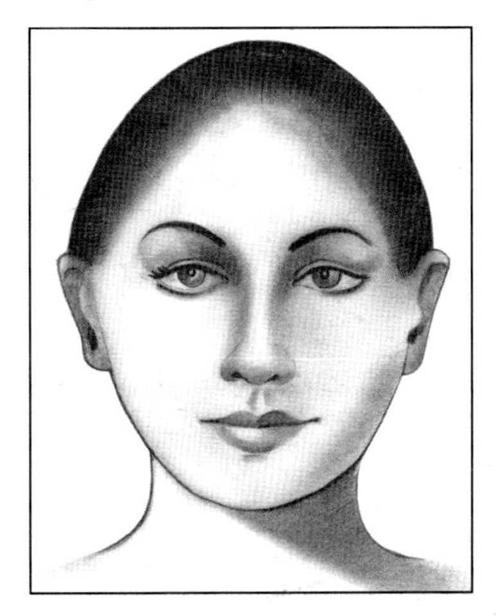

7. Long Face :

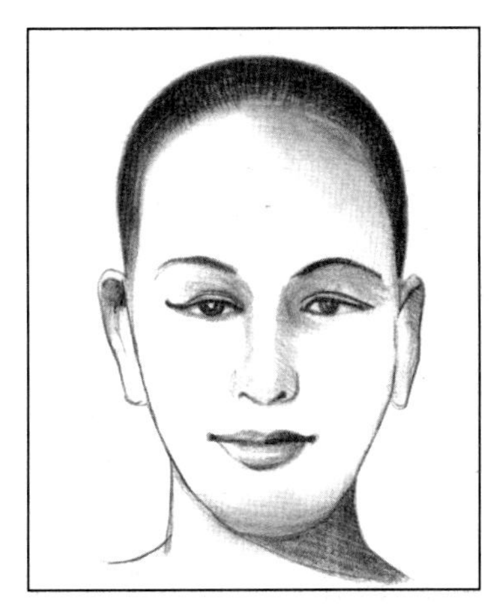

To make each of these faces perfect, make-up is done after doing the face-cut. It is called shading. This shading is done with dark colours like black and brown. To make each of these faces perfect, make the Oval Face by face-cutting.

* **Caretaking :** Dark shade is used to hide the hill part of the face which is called shading.

Light shade is used to give the face a hill look to the valley part. It is called highlighting.

The raised part of the face is called the 'hill' and the sunken part is called the 'valley'. Highlighting is done on the hill-part. Problems are seen more in the valley-parts, as : Circles under eyes, Pigmentation, Pimple-marks, Acne, etc..

Hills :

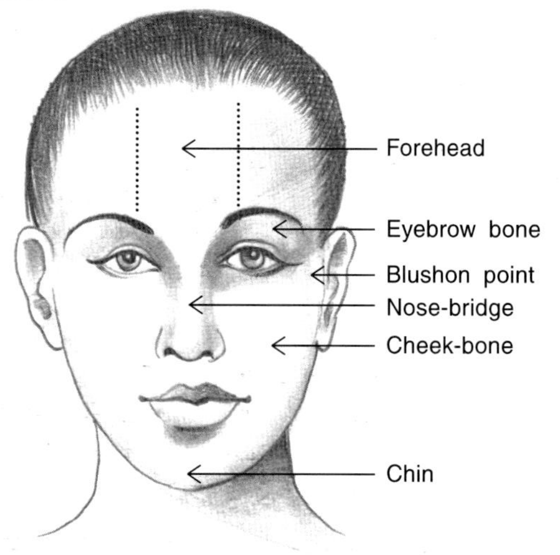

Valleies :

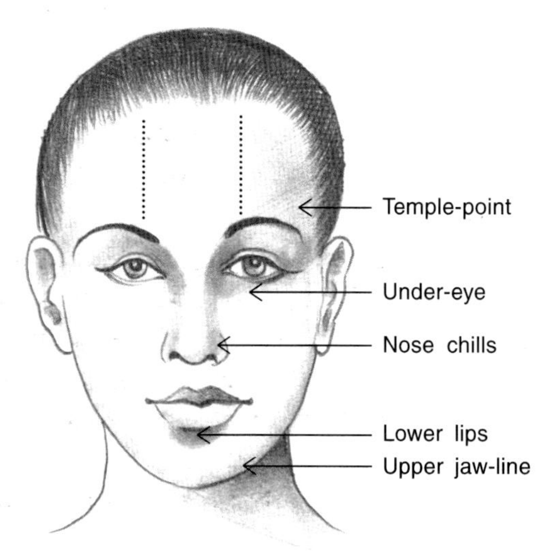

* Face-cutting is done with the dark concealer negro 1, 2, the black-brown pencil, terra cotta and the black-brown eyeshadow.

(2) Skin Colour

Generally, Skin has four colour tones :

1. Fair Skin 2. Wheatish Skin 3. Dark Wheatish Skin 4. Very Dark Wheatish Skin :

Concealer is selected according to the skin-tone :

1. Fair Skin : For this type of skin, FS series concealers are used. FS means Fair Skin. The numbers for FS series concealers are 22, 28, 29, 38, 626 A, 626 B, etc..

2. Wheatish Skin : Wheatish skin concealers are FS 25, 36, 40, 626 C, etc..

3. Dark Wheatish Skin : This type of skin has a little darker tone than that of the Wheatish Skin. For this skin, the numbers of the concealers are FS 24, Chinese, LE (Light Egyptian), 626 D, 46, etc..

4. Very Dark Wheatish Skin : For this type of skin, the concealers are FS 27, DE (Dark Egyptian), Negro 1, Negro 2, 665 G, 665 F, etc..

* **Concealers are used to cover the skin problems. These concealers are of five types :**

➢ Yellow = Yellow (303) → Fair Skin

➢ D 32 → For dark skin like the Negro. This concealer is to be applied before doing the base. It gives glow.

➢ Chinese → For the circles under eyes in dark skin

➢ 561 → For quite fair skin – to make the deep portion below the eye look risen.

➢ Negro → For face-cutting

All the shades except the above-mentioned ones are called foundation.

(3) Skin Concept

Make-up varies from occasion to occasion. For example, Light matt effect make-up is for the daytime, while the heavy base and the glittery make-up is done at the night.

* **Materials used for Make-up :**

➢ Concealer, Moisturizer

➢ Panstick (Concealer, Cream Foundation)

➢ Pancake (Water base, Dry cake)

➢ Translucent Powder (White, Yellow, Ivory, Pink)

➢ Water-spray (Rosewater, eau-de-Cologne water)

➢ Muslin cloth

➢ Shimmer Powder (Pink, Bronze, Silver, Golden)

➢ Eyeshadow (Powder-shadow, Pigment, Cream base)

➢ Highlighter (Golden, Silver)

➢ Eyeliner (Pencil, Cream, Liquid, Gel, Cake and Powder)

➢ Eyebrow defining powder (Black, Brown Pencil)

➢ Mascara (Black, Brown Transparent, Zoom, Fibre, Primer)

➢ Blusher, Blushon (Pink, Light Brown, Dark Brown, Maroon, Orange)

➢ Lipstick

* **Types of Make-up Brush :**

➢ Polishing Brush

➢ Powder Brush

➢ Blushon Brush

➢ Eyeliner Brush

➢ Mascara Brush

➢ Flat Brush (Shading and Highlighting)

➢ Eyebrow Brush

➢ Eyeshadow Applicator Brush

➢ Lipliner Brush

➢ Lipfiller Brush

➢ Fan Brush

* **Taking care while doing the Make-up :**

➢ It is very important to make the face clean before the make-up. If there is dead skin, remove the dead skin, and then allow the make-up.

➢ If there is unwanted hair left in the eyebrows, go for the threading first before the make-up.

➢ If there is more hair on the face, get the bleaching done first.

➢ Go for one shade light make-up or one shade dark make-up than the skin-tone.

➢ Go for dry-base make-up in summer; go for the moisture base make-up in winter.

➢ Use the make-up of a good quality.

➢ Insist on using only the water-proof eyeliner and mascara.

➢ Clean the brushes after every make-up.

➢ Clean the sponge with antiseptic after the make-up, so that the possibility of infection can be clearly avoided.

➢ Do the deep cleansing with face-wash astringent in the oily skin, with the cleansing milk in the dry skin and with a scrub if there is a lot of dead skin.

➢ Spread the concealer with light weight because if it is done with heavy weight, the make-up gets patchy.

➢ Don't apply ice before the make-up because the application of ice closes the skin-pores temporarily. But after the effect of the ice is over, once more the pores open up and the make-up gives a patchy look or it spreads all over the face.

(4) Methods of Make-up

1. Single Base Make-up 2. Double Base Make-up

1. Single Base Make-up :

➢ Clean the face befitting the type of skin.

➢ Cover the face problems like dark circles under eyes, spots of pimples, pigmentation, etc., with the matching concealer.

➢ Use the translucent powder befitting the skin-tone.

➢ Go for the matching eyeshadow befitting the costume. Apply a thin layer of the highlighter.

➢ Define the eyebrow with the eyebrow pencil.

➢ Apply the waterproof eyeliner.

➢ Apply the blusher in the matching tone.

➢ Apply the waterproof mascara.

➢ If needed, stick a *bindi*.

➢ Apply a light or dark lipstick befitting the occasion.

2. Double Base Make-up :

➢ Clean the face befitting the skin type.

➢ Cover the face problems like the dark circles under eyes, spots of pimples, pigmentation, etc., with the matching concealer befitting the skin.

➢ Apply the matching concealer on the entire face and spread it.

➢ Apply a thin layer of the matching pancake mixed with water befitting the skin-tone.

➢ After the pancake dries off, even it with the sponge and spray water. Then dab it with the muslin cloth.

➢ Apply the shimmer powder on the highlighting point.

➢ Do the eyeshadow befitting the costume and apply the highlighter.

➢ Define the eyebrow.

➢ Do the waterproof eyeliner.

➢ If needed, stick a *bindi*.

➢ Use a light or dark lipstick befitting the function.

(5) Different Types of Make-up

1. Golden Make-up :

➢ Clean the face befitting the skin type.

➢ Apply the panstick befitting the face matching tone.

➢ Then apply the translucent powder.

➢ Dab with a wet muslin cloth.

➢ Do the polishing with the compact golden-gloss powder.

➢ Dab with a dry muslin cloth.

➢ Apply the matching eyeshadow in the eyesocket area. Then apply the golden eyeshadow on the eyeball. Apply the golden highlighter.

[**Golden Make-up**]

➢ Do eyeliner with the eyebrow pencil.

➢ Apply the brown-black zoom mascara.

➢ Apply the reddish brown blusher and if needed stick a *bindi*.

➢ Use the matching lipstick and do the highlighting with the golden pigment in the middle part of the lips.

2. Silver Make-up :

➢ Clean the face befitting the skin type.

➢ Apply the silver base cream on the entire face with light weight.

➢ Do the face-cutting befitting the skin matching tone.

➢ Apply the concealer befitting the skin matching tone in the part where face cutting is not done.

➢ Apply the translucent powder befitting the skin matching tone.

[**Silver Make-up**]

➢ Do the water-spray (eau-de-Cologne water + Rosewater + Water) and dab with the muslin cloth.

➢ Apply the silver-gloss powder or the silver blusher on the highlighting point. Then dab it with the dry muslin cloth.

➢ Apply the silver eyeshadow in the area from the eyeliner to the eyebrow. Apply the pink eyeshadow in the front part of the eye and the black eyeshadow in the back part of the eye.

➢ Define the eyebrow with the eyebrow defining powder and do the liquid eye-liner.

➢ Do the splash-proof mascara.

➢ Do the pink blusher. If needed, stick a *bindi*.

➢ Apply the silver liquid base lipstick on the lips and do the pink eyeliner on it.

3. Bronze Make-up :

[Bronze Make-up]

➢ Clean the face befitting the skin type.

➢ Cover the face problems with the matching concealer.

➢ Mix the bronze powder in the matching tone pancake and apply a thin layer of it on the entire face.

➢ Apply the face matching tone concealer.

➢ Dab with a wet muslin cloth.

➢ Do polishing with the deep bronze powder on the highlighting point.

➢ Dab with a dry muslin cloth.

➢ Apply the bronze colour pigment on the eyelid and do the eyeshadow in the middle part of the eyelid befitting the colour matching. Then do the black eyeshadow in the corner. Apply the highlighter.

➢ Define the eyebrow and do the black-cake eyeliner.

[Bronze Make-up]

➢ Do the brown bronze blusher and the medium black long mascara.

➢ Do the nude transparent lipstick and apply the lip-gel upon it.

4. Corrective Make-up :

➢ Clean the face befitting the skin type.

➢ Do the face-cutting with the black-brown pencil as suggested in different face-graphs on the page Nos. 90, 91 and 92.

➢ Cover the face-problems with the matching concealer.

➢ Do the face-matching tone concealing in the part where face-cutting is not done.

➢ Apply the skin-matching translucent powder and dab with a wet muslin cloth.

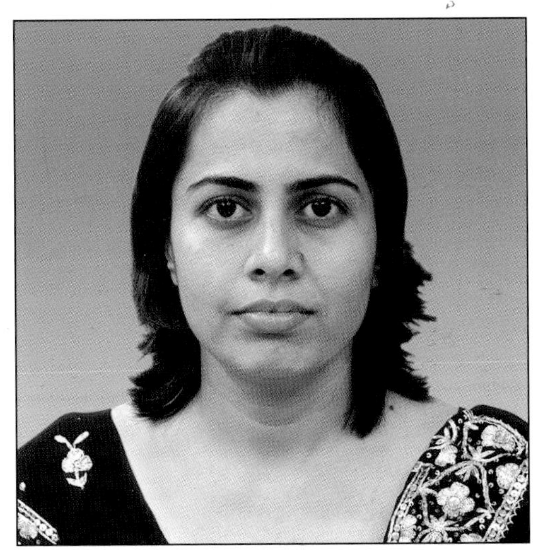

[Face – before Make-up]

[Face – after Make-up]

➢ Do the peach-gold eyeshadow from the eyeliner line to the eyebrow. Do the light black line from the eye-ending to the eyebrow ending. Merge the black inwards in the eyesocket area.

➢ Do a line with the black eyeshadow below the eye and do the black eyeliner.

➢ Define the eyebrow and do the volume mascara.

➢ Do the brown blusher on the face-cutting part and slant the pink blusher above it. Do the silver highlighting above it.

➢ Do the highlighting with the silver shimmer powder on the other high-lighting part.

➢ If needed, stick a *bindi*.

➢ Do the light lipstick and apply the transparent lip-gloss.

5. Bridal Make-up :

➢ Clean the face befitting the skin type.

➢ Spray the make-up fixer from the distance of two feet.

➢ Cover the face problems with the matching concealer.

➢ Do the face-cutting.

➢ Apply the translucent powder.

➢ Make the pancake of face matching tone and apply its thin layer on the entire face. Even it with the sponge after the pancake dries off.

➢ Do the water-spray and dab with a dry muslin cloth.

➢ Do the polishing with the shimmer powder on the highlighting point.

➢ Do the eyeshadow with the maroon colour or with the matching tone of the clothes in the eyesocket area. Do the eyeshadow with golden, silver or with the copper colour pigment on the eye-ball. Do the contouring with the green or grey eyeshadow in the eye-ending area.

➢ Do the golden or the silver high-lighter.

➢ Define the eyebrow and apply the transparent mascara on it.

➢ Apply the waterproof cake eyeliner.

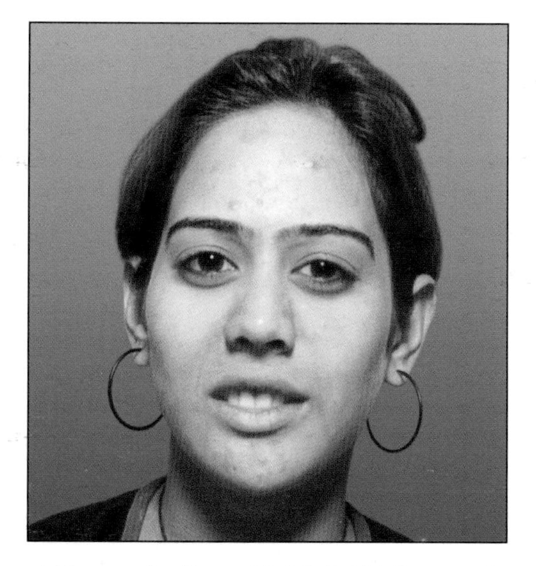

[Face – before Bridal Make-up]

[Face – after Bridal Make-up]

➢ Do the volume mascara.

➢ Do the brown blusher in the hollow of the check part, the maroon blusher in the part above it and the highlighting in the part still above it.

➢ Do the *peer* and stick a *bindi*.

➢ Do the lipstick of the matching shade and do highlighting with the golden, silver or copper colour pigment in the centre part of the lips.

[Face – before Bridal Make-up]

[Face – after Bridal Make-up]

6. Reception Make-up :

➢ Clean the face befitting the skin type.

➢ Apply the bronzer with light weight on the entire face.

➢ Cover the face problems with the matching concealer.

➢ Apply the face matching tone concealer in less quantity.

[Reception Make-up]

➢ Do the face-cutting with the black-brown pencil.

➢ Apply the translucent powder.

➢ Mix the shimmer powder in the face-tone matching the pancake and apply the thin layer all over the face. Dab with sponge after the pancake dries off.

➢ Dab with a wet muslin cloth.

➢ Do polishing with the shimmer powder all over the face.

➢ Do contouring with the pink eye-shadow in the inner corner of the eye, with the orange eyeshadow in the middle and with the blue eyeshadow in the outer corner of the eye. Do the golden colour pigment in the centre on the eyelid (over the eyeball) and allow a little glitter on it.

➢ Do the golden or silver glitter highlighter.

➢ Define the eyebrow and do the eye-liner. Do the eyeliner a little away from the eye.

➢ Do the blusher of the matching tone and do the glitter on the highlighting-point.

➢ Do the volume mascara and stick a *bindi*.

➢ Do the matching lipstick and do the liquid lipstick on it.

7. D. J. Party Make-up :

➢ Clean the face according to the skin type.

➢ Cover the face-problems with the matching concealer.

➢ Apply the dry cake and do the thin layer of the pancake on it. Even the layer with the sponge after the pancake dries off.

➢ Do the water-spray and dab with a muslin cloth.

➢ Do the polishing with the shimmer powder all over the face.

➢ Do the peach-gold eyeshadow on the eye. Do the thick eyeliner with the black shadow at the eyeliner. Then smuge it upwards with the smuger. Extend the black eyeshadow outwards so as to make the eyes look longer. Do the liner with the powder shadow below the eye.

➢ Define the eyebrow and do the volume mascara.

➢ Do the pink blusher.

➢ Apply the nude lipstick.

➢ Do the multi-glitter spray on the entire face keeping the distance of about two feet after the hairstyle, the make-up and the dressing is over.

[D. J. Party Make-up]

8. Engagement Make-up :

➢ Clean the face according to the skin type.

➢ Cover the face problems with the matching concealer.

➢ Apply the liquid base foundation on the entire face.

➢ Do the polishing with dry cake and dab with a wet muslin cloth.

[Engagement Make-up]

➢ Do the light eyeshadow befitting the matching tone and do the light highlighting.

➢ Define the eyebrow and do the eye-liner.

➢ Do the matching blusher and the mascara.

➢ Stick a matching *bindi*.

➢ Apply the lipstick. If needed, do the lip-gloss.

DIFFERENT EYE MAKE-UPS

SECTION 8 : SAREE-STYLES

(1)

[Gujarati Saree]

(1) Gujarati Saree

Wrap one round of the opposite edge of the hem *(palav, pallu)* around the waist. Then fold the *palav* in equal folds. Take the folded *palav*-edge back from the left side and bring it up on the right shoulder. Let the *palav* drop in the front. Pin it up on the right shoulder.

Now, back to the waist. Fold the middle part of the saree in equal folds and push in the folded part in the front, in the centre of the waist. Take back the loose *palav*-edge from (dropping in) the front and pin it up with the blouse.

* **Note :** Any saree with good design in the *palav* looks decent in Gujarati Saree-style.

(2) Simple Bengali Saree

Wrap one round of the opposite edge of the *palav* around the waist. Then take the folded *palav*-edge back from the right side and bring it up onto the left shoulder. Let the *palav* drop to the required length at the back. Then pin it up on the left shoulder.

Now, back to the waist. Fold the middle part of the saree in equal folds and push in the folded part on the right side of the waist. The *palav*-edge with equal folds can be pinned-up on the left shoulder or can be left loose (unfolded) according to your choice.

* **Note :** Only the saree with work on its border or a quite plain one gives young look in this Bengali Saree-style.

(2)

[Simple Bengali Saree]

[Necklace Saree]

(3) Necklace Saree

This saree-style greatly resembles Burmese saree-style. In the Burmese saree-style, the *palav*-edge is left loose dropping in the front from the right shoulder.

In this style, as shown in the photograph, (as the border is clearly displayed) let the *palav*-border edge go round the neck. The round will go from the back right side to the back left side. Let that edge drop at the back, almost up to the waist. It will give the look as is shown in the photograph beside.

* **Note :** In this saree-style, since the saree-border goes around the neck, it gives the look of a Necklace. In this style, it is a must to have a saree with a good designed border.

(4) Wrap-around Saree

Wrap one round of the opposite edge of the *palav* around the waist. Then fold the *palav*-edge in equal folds. Now, attach safety-pins to the *palav*-edge at the equal distance (approx – two feet each) till the saree-border gets over. Then take the loose round of the pinned *palav*-edge from the left side on the waist and bring it to the front from the right side. Take three more loose rounds in the same way and bring the loose end onto the left shoulder. Let it drop loose at the back. Now, from among these three rounds on the waist, pull the lowest one after taking out pins from it and set it as is shown in the photograph. Then pull another that is just above the lowest one and set it a little above the lowest one. Then pull the uppermost (whose edge goes over to the left shoulder) and set it a little above the two lower ones. Keep a proper distance vertically so that the saree-border looks as is shown in the photograph beside. Leave the loose edge dropping from the left shoulder. Don't pin it on the shoulder.

* **Note :** For this style, only the saree with a decent border can serve the purpose. This style looks gorgeous on a slim-figured woman.

[Wrap-around Saree]

[**Burmese Saree**]

(5) Burmese Saree

Wrap two rounds of the opposite edge of the *palav* around the waist. Then fold the *palav*-edge in equal folds. Bring the folded *palav*-edge on the right shoulder from the back side. Then let it drop till below the knees in the front. Now, bring the lowest fold further to the front from the backside through below the left hand. Then take on the same fold-end from below the right hand to the backside. Once more bring it to the front from below the left hand. Then fold it. Push in those folds on the waist behind the previously set saree-border. Set the raised saree-border once more. Thus, the saree-border dropping from the right shoulder and the side-border coming in the front from the back will give the look as it is shown in the photograph beside.

* **Note :** In this style, the saree-border drops from the right shoulder till below the knees. It gives a gorgeous look. For this style, a saree with a good designed border is essential.

(6) Bengali or *Devdas* Saree

Start wrapping the opposite edge of *palav* from the left side of the waist. Finish one round and bring it to the front in the second round. Then take the long edge of the *palav* from the front to the left shoulder and let it drop till a good length at the back. Pin it up on the left shoulder. Now, fold the middle part of the saree into one or two folds and push it in to the right side on waist. Then pull the lowest fold of the border folds, take it back to the right side and pin it up with the blouse. At last, bring in the front the long edge of the *palav* from the back and pin it up on the right shoulder.

* **Note :** Right from the shoulders, almost up to the ankles this saree-style gives V shape, so it looks very attractive. For this style, only the saree with a good designed border can serve the purpose.

[**Bengali or *Devdas* Saree**]

[**Gown Saree**]

(7) Gown Saree

Wrap one round of the opposite edge of the *palav* around the waist. Then take the *palav*-edge back from the left side and bring it to the front from the right side on to the waist. Fold the middle part of the saree into 8 to 10 equal folds and push it on the waist in the front. Then take the remaining end from the right side covering over the blouse and bring it back from below the left hand. Bring the end 5 to 6 inches low in the front and pin it up on the right shoulder as well as with the border edge of the saree whose round-wrapping has already been done.

* **Note :** This saree-style lends the look like that of a western gown, which is really eye-catching.

(8) 7 Up Saree

Wrap one round of the opposite edge of the *palav*. Then fold it in some equal folds. Take the *palav*-edge on to the left shoulder from the back making it pass from below the right hand. Take this end at the back behind the left shoulder (approx 4 to 5 inches) and pin it up with the blouse. Now, fold the middle part of the saree in equal folds. Twist these folds all together 2 to 3 times and push them in to the left side of the waist. It gives the 7 up look as is shown in the photograph beside.

* **Note :** In this style, the saree-border that is pinned-up on the back side behind the left shoulder, keeps dropping straight till below the knees. It gives the look of the English cardinal number 7, so this saree-style is so called. Select the saree with an attractive border for this style.

[**7 Up Saree**]

(9)

[Waterfall Saree]

(9) Waterfall Saree

Put on the traditional Gujarati saree. The *palav* must be falling from the right shoulder in the front. Extend it till the knees. Fold the middle part of the saree in 8 to 10 equal folds. Split the folds into two equal sections. Push in these double folds in the equally double width on the waist. (It is called Box-split.) Now, make small pinches of the *palav* dropping till below the knees, and pin them up with the safety-pins starting from the right shoulder. Go on pinning-up the pinches in a half-circle from below the neck a little below the left shoulder. This pinches-circle from a little below the right shoulder to a little below the left shoulder in half-circle gives the look of a necklace.

* **Note :** This style gives an unusually decent look. For this style, any chiffon, georget, etc., sarees will serve the purpose.

(10) Double Saree

Take two sarees. Put on one Gujarati saree at first. Now, before putting on the other saree, fold the *palav* into equal folds. Keep these folds of the *palav* dropping from the left shoulder in the front, parallel to the Gujarati saree. Then the remaining long end of this saree is to be passed in through the edge of the Gujarati saree which is already taken up on the right shoulder. Then bring it to the front on the waist. Since this edge is very long, many folds can be formed off it. Thus, those folds will be more and larger than those of a common saree edge. Now, push in these larger folds on the waist to the right side i.e., exactly on the opposite side of the folds of the Gujarati saree (have been pushed in). It gives a double look like that of a '*chaniya-choli*' and of a 'saree'.

* **Note :** The saree other than the Gujarati saree should be of a thin material. For this style, the saree without border is preferred.

(10)

[Double Saree]

(11)

[Border-line Saree]

(11) Border-line Saree

Wrap one round of the opposite edge of the *palav* of the saree. Then fold the *palav* in equal folds. Take this *palav*-edge back from the right side and bring it on to the left shoulder from the back. Pin-up the edge of the left shoulder letting it drop in the front. Now, fold the middle part of the saree in some equal folds and push that part into the left side or to the right side on the waist, according to the convenience.

Now, unfold the folds of the edge on the left shoulder. Once more fold it into vertical folds as the border should be displayed outside clearly (as shown in the photograph beside). Then let the edge drop in the front from the left shoulder till below the knee and pin it up.

* **Note :** This style looks quite decent because of its vertical border. Only the saree with a well-designed border can serve the purpose.

(12) Traditional with Western Saree

This style greatly resembles the Bengali or *Devdas* style. It is not at all required to make equal folds of the middle part of the saree. Leave it loose. Instead of pinning-up the *palav*-edge on the right shoulder, bring it to the front from below the right hand. Now, pin-up the end with the blouse 4 to 5 inches below the left shoulder. Raise the *palav*-border dropping from the left shoulder a little to pin-up the end with the blouse. This will give a look of three borders in the front as shown in the photograph beside. Then push in the middle part of the loose edge on the right side of the waist. It should be pushed in below the borders. It will bring in U shape look as shown in the photograph beside.

* **Note :** The saree with an attractive border is essential for this style.

(12)

[Traditional with Western Saree]

PICTURES OF THE VARIETIES OF *PEER* AND *BINDIS*

* **Note :** ➢ *Peer-Bindi* is done with *Shringar* and Water-colour.
  ➢ For *Peer* and *Bindi*, the brushes – Nos. 0 and 1 are used.
  ➢ To make *Peer* and *Bindi* look proper and better, enlarged pictures are given here. In fact, there will be quite tiny design on the face.

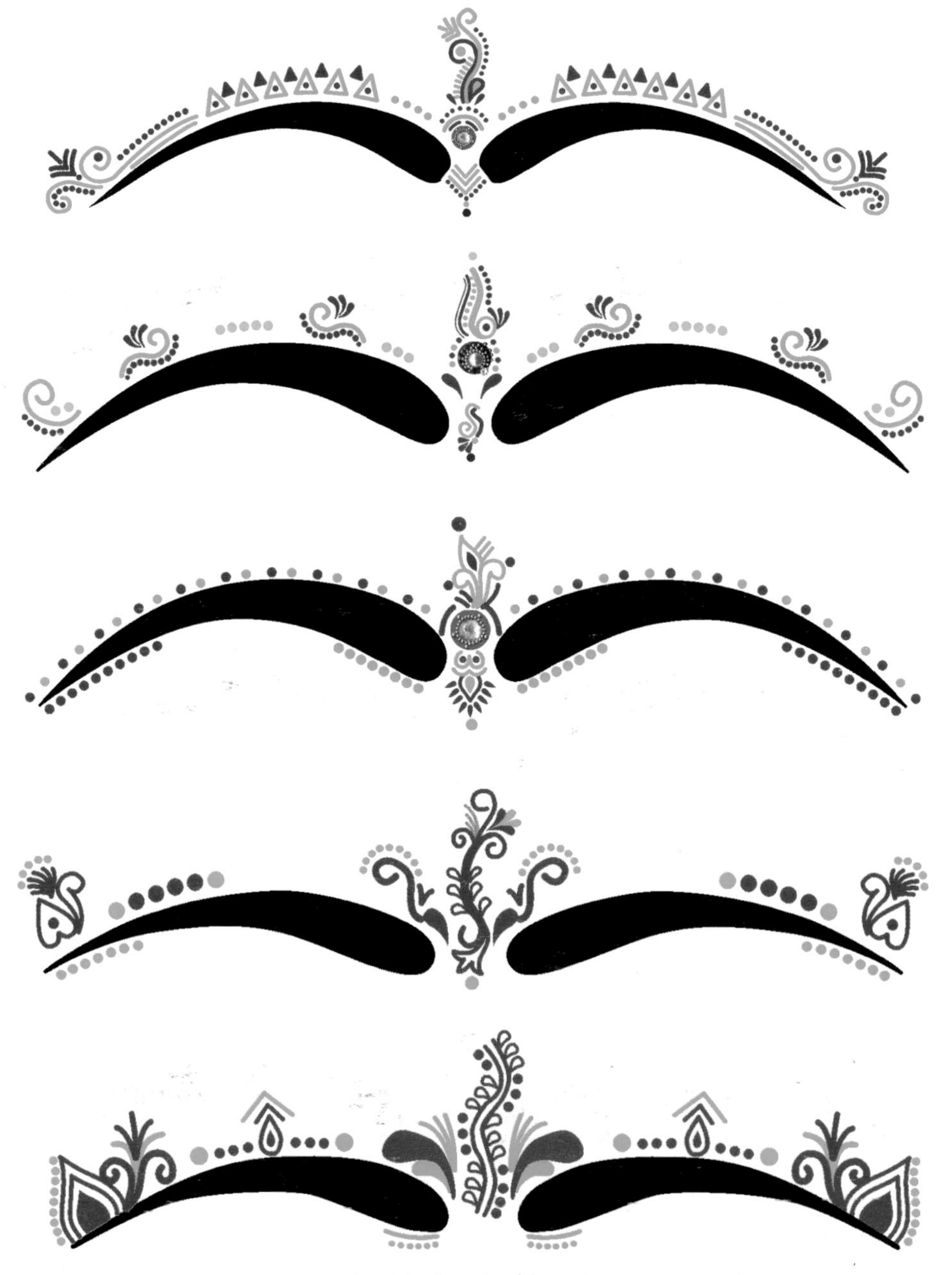

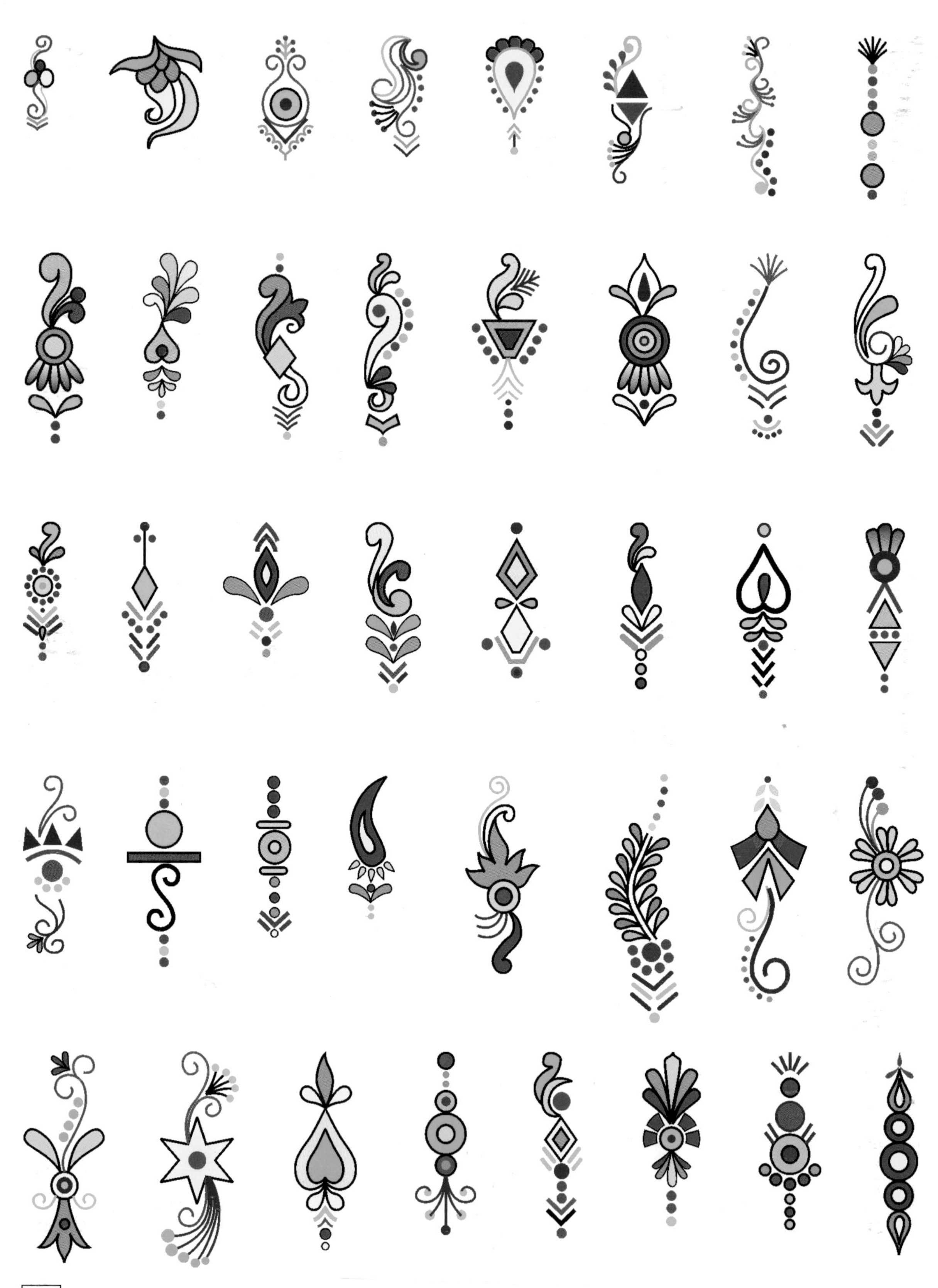

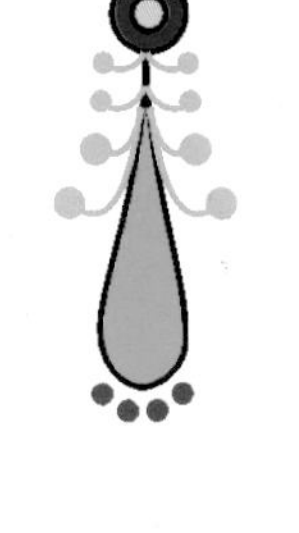

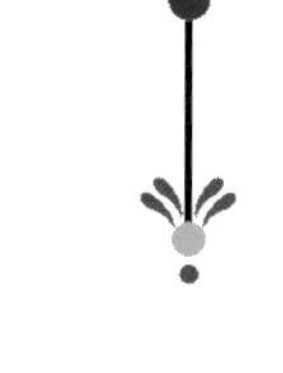

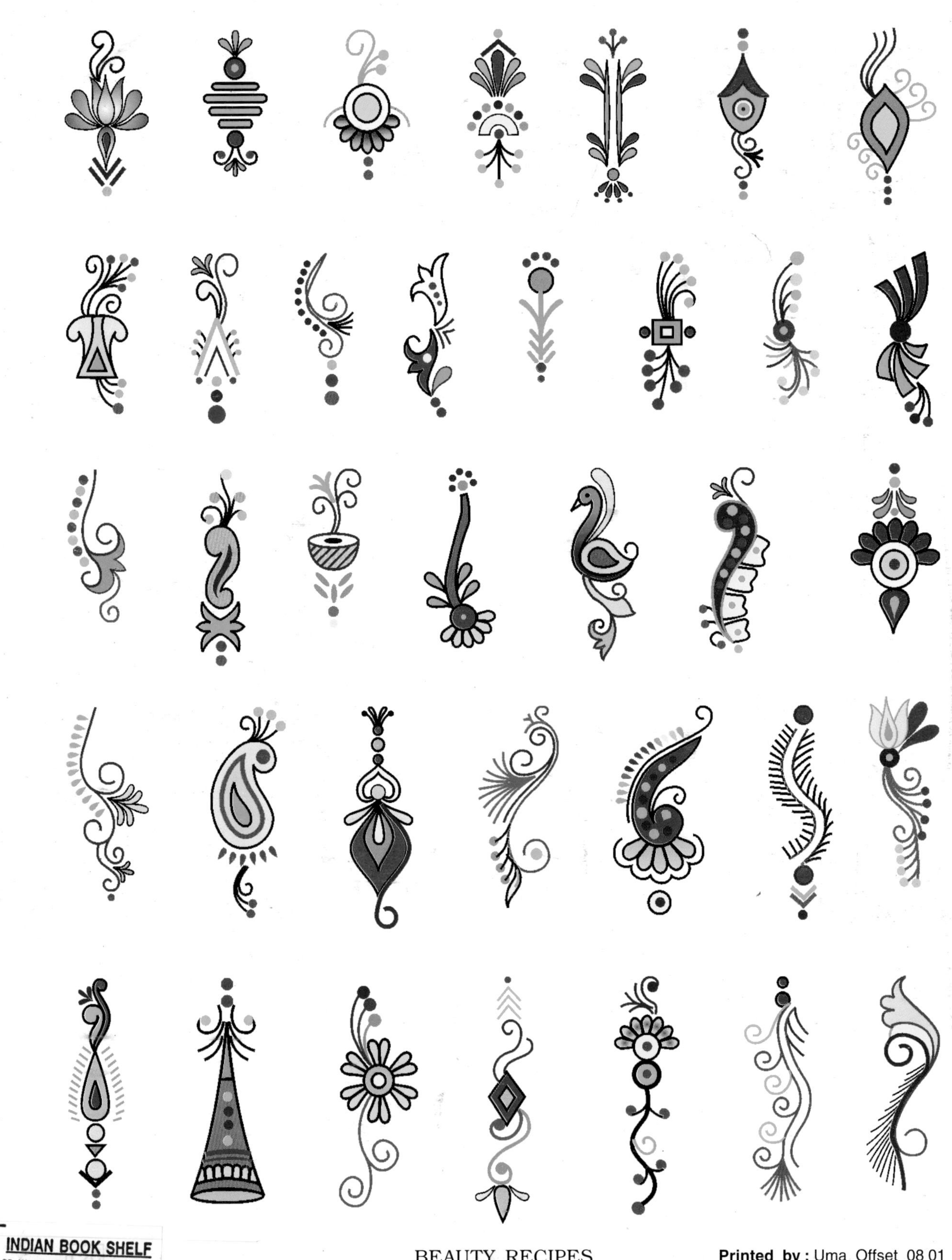

Printed by : Uma Offset 08 01